WELLSPRING:

The Energy Secrets TO DO The Good Life

Jason Littleton, MD

WELLSPRING HUMAN ENERGETICS, LLC
Inspiration • Concentration • Execution

1st Edition
WellSpring: The Energy Secrets To Do the Good Life
Copyright © 2012 Jason Littleton, MD
WellSpring Human Energetics, LLC
www.wellspringhumanenergetics.com

Cover design: Helize Vivier, CREATE180Design
Cover Photographer: Allison Streeter
Editor: Erin Ford, InkDot Edits
ISBN: 978-0-9857476-0-2

This book is dedicated to my pastors, Drs. James and Stacia Pierce (who is also my business coach). Without them this would not be possible nor would I have reached this place in life—period. To Dr. Stacia, my invaluable coach who has the vision to see much more in me than I do myself—and the ability to bring it out of me—this book is especially dedicated to you.

To my wife, Rheami, the woman of my dreams and my best friend, I dedicate this book to you, for everything I do you are the co-pilot, whether directly or indirectly. You help bring about every success I have.

To my parents, Dr. Ray and Marcia Littleton, who have sacrificed time, money—energy to bring me up and support me through my formal years of training, this book is also dedicated to you.

To the Ford family—Aristotle, Erin and Asher, thank you. Thank you Erin (my editor and Senior Editor of InkDotEdits) for your relentless efforts in making my book perfect.

To all my friends, family, and to you my readers, who (like me) know there is something more to living an energized-fulfilled healthy life; this book is dedicated to U.

Table of Contents

Introduction

Boarding

Bottom line: You're tired. And that's why you're here. I get it. I've been there too. It's a place of frustration; sometimes despair. *Tiredness* is a place where hopelessness can set in—hopelessness of ever completing your goals or arriving at that other place called *Satisfaction* for completion of a goal or a to-do list.

More and more I have found in practice and in life that people never arrive or fully complete some of the most earnest goals/dreams they have, leaving a void of despair or failure that only leads to them being more and more unsatisfied. I have observed that this usually is the result of the lack of three core things: 1. Inspiration 2. Concentration 3. Execution. Or in a word, I.C.E.

Come in closer and let me make myself vitally clear: You do not just want more energy. But that's what you think you want. You don't realize it but you've been there already and you're tired of that too. You want passion that moves you; that gets you out of bed and causes you to work when your body's fuel is depleted. *That's inspiration!*

Some of you are tired of just not connecting the dots in life. Dots are important because dots are the benchmarks that tell us we are getting closer to our destination. And when you are in the place in between dots it can be hard to tell if you're in between or off course. Not knowing is exhausting in itself mentally because you don't know if you are wasting precious energy and time or if you are right on point. You want radar, or the internal sense that you are where you are supposed to be, doing what you are supposed to be doing, so that you don't waste your allotted energy. *That's concentration!*

When it's all said and done, we are looking for outcomes—results! And in order to get results and move from dot to dot—point A to point B—we need a tangible supply of human fuel. Fuel that we can process and turn into results. It's not enough to just have stored energy. You have to release it! Pour it out! Let it go! In other words, turn the throttle up and burn the fuel (create a void so more will come)! *That's execution!*

As we know, ice is simply H_2O in solid form. In solid form, the energy lies in the chemical bonds. In order to release that energy, you have to heat the ice, or *burn it up*. When one burns the ice, the atoms connected by the chemical bonds become farther and farther apart until the bonds are broken and theenergy is released. This transitions ice from a solid to a liquid and finally a gas, where there no longer is an H_2O structure but only hydrogen and oxygen atoms flying around in space. Ice is in essence stored fuel. We have to *burn it up* to release it!

One of the clients I often see is the depressed or down-trodden client. As a family practitioner, at times, treating depression and anxiety can be close to 50 percent of my practice! I've come to realize that not having a merry heart can not only zap the energy out of your life, but it can zap your joy. Depression is a serious clinical and personal entity that needs to be treated multi-factorially. I have found that a lot of my patients who struggle with depression also struggle with fatigue and goal accomplishment. This form of tiredness may not exactly feel like the tiredness of being on your feet all day, but it's a close relative in the same family. For the most part, some of my patients with this condition have trouble just getting on their feet. Getting out of bed—or the desire to not get out of bed *to do*—is one of the top five things I hear when I am evaluating depression in a person. A trend I've noticed is that most succumb to feelings of demotivation so much so that it's hard to look above the clouds and see the sun. I have some patients where it's not just partly cloudy, but it's cloudy all the time and seeing the sun is a fairytale in the sweet by and by.

What I try to do is simple: I try to give them a carrot to eat. I try to be that person for a time who holds the stick with the carrot on the end to motivate them to get up and *to do*. The carrot is their true dreams and desires that I am helping them put out in front of them so they can get on their feet and start heading toward *the dots* or benchmarks, which leads to goal achievement, and also, *Satisfaction*.

Still there is another type of client I am writing this book for: the person who feels the brunt of the rat race, often feeling down-and-out—frustrated that they can never catch up, and losing confidence that they ever will. To them, life is about surviving; getting through the day. "Thank God it's Friday," and "Oh no, it's Monday." These are the types who know Wednesday as Hump Day and the weekend as Rest Time, feeling sluggish and often frustrated after a long week with tons of effort, yet still disappointed of not accomplishing fully that which was set out to do (not only because of physical energy depletion).

A lot of times it's mental energy or concentration that is missing, where you are busy doing a lot of things yet not making effective progress toward your benchmarks. When you are in this type of mode, you have lost control on what matters most. You are unorganized mentally. And in this type of state it is impossible to connect the dots in your life. Things must be streamlined and until they are, what happens is your allotted energy reserve catches up to your wasted energy and time, and you find yourself depleted and in the place called Tired. When this happens time and time again, you wonder if you'll ever get a grip on things; ever catch your breath in order to get in control of your world. The frustration exists because now you have entered an insane cycle of never getting things done, losing confidence that you ever will.

Lastly I want to digress a bit about the final energy secret to do the good life—*execution*. To execute anything, you need fuel or energy. Yet it is the release of that fuel or energy that generates the corresponding actions. Releasing energy is always an act of the will because it takes a decision to choose what type of corresponding actions you will perform. I want to say a word about human fuel or energy matter first before I go on, because I know this is what we think we are looking for. I want you to understand that the desire for more energy truly is a fad. The truth of the matter is the *type* of energy or *quality* of fuel that we expend and *how* it's spent is the key, and not the *amount* of energy we have.

In other words, it's not the amount of gas we have; it's the quality and the way we spend it that matters. A car's fuel tank has a limited capacity. And like I said, you've been there and you're tired of it. Currently we are in a time where the energy drink filled with caffeine and other artificial products is routinely relied upon to get one through the day or to help cross our to-dos off our list. But what is happening is more and more products are being put on the market with higher levels of caffeine, to override the semi-tolerance that is building up amongst us in order for us to feel rejuvenated. Dissatisfaction is kicking in, but some don't realize it and that's why the energy drink industry is growing and growing.

I was talking with a close friend and client the other day about the sense of fatigue he has been experiencing in the midst of great job-related tasks still needing to be done. The problem was that his job requirements call for him to perform on sometimes minimal/nonexistent sleep while still being mentally sharp to function on a top-flight level. Honestly, he admitted to using higher-tiered, caffeinated energy drinks to help him rise above his fatigue, still lacking an answer to his overwhelming acknowledgment that soon the floor is going to come out from beneath him and he'll be left wanting for the next latest and greatest source to help him achieve on such a high level.

Like my friend, you too, I'm sure, have been there. More energy is what my friend was looking for by escalating the consumption of the latest and greatest advertised caffeinated drink; and yet, never quite feeling completely energized.

And even still, let's take the caffeinated energy drink crusade even further. How about this case: the case of the intern on call, doing a 30-hour shift twice a week with regular working hours in between. Now caffeine is no longer a drink consumed, but instead another prophylactic medication simply administered to keep one going through the shift; used again post-call as an eye-opener because of the latent sleep and off-cycled circadian rhythms. No longer does he care about inspiration, concentration, execution; the things it took to become a medical doctor. In the face of tiredness, even patient care is an afterthought. No sense of satisfaction dwells here. Dreams, goals and aspirations are blurred by duties, hours, obligations and pure grade-A exhaustion, a.k.a intern burnout—a real entity. I know because that was me.

Like I said in the beginning, I get it. I too have been to this place called Tiredness. I pitched my tent, made my bed and laid down there only to wake up still tired and not having energy *to do* life—my life.

And here's the key: What I learned is that in order to overcome or depart this place of Tiredness *to do* the good life, you have to let go of the defense mechanism causing you to preserve your energy. You have to overcome the fear of having nothing left. Having nothing left is a good place to be—not to lay down and sleep there, but instead to be filled with anticipation of what's to come. Get ready, for the place you just created is the space where new energy can now rush in and fill the void with even greater energy. Not only greater in quality but now also quantity; for the principle of energy release guarantees a higher volume of energy return. Operating in this principle continually enacts or impels an inexhaustible source and supply of energy, which can be harnessed *to do* your life. This source and supply is called the *WellSpring*.

As the struggling intern suffering from burnout, I realized I needed to reset. I needed to enact an energy WellSpring of currency through my life *to do* my life.

Please understand this too: Creating a WellSpring in your life is also about arriving. A lot of times people do not want to say "I have arrived." But this type of thinking can be wrong if always used. There are seasons for everything and just like there are seasons to depart, there are seasons to arrive. Arriving is a way of goal achievement. Arriving is how your joy may be full.

I have always loved airplanes. A lot of times when I am working with clients when treating a psychological disorder, I often refer to the airplane in terms of its ability for flight, in order to metaphorically relate to our attribute *to do* life. But that's not all. I refer to airplanes when I am trying to help the depressed see above the clouds.

As human beings, we are a spirit, with a soul, in a body. Our spirits needs inspiration and our soul—encompassing our mind, will, intellect, imagination and emotions—must be controlled in order to concentrate. And of course, when all is said and done, our bodies must be moved to *execute*—*to do* our lives. When it comes to function, in part, we were created *to do* or to achieve.

I want you to come fly with me as I take you on a journey where I will help you discover how to create your WellSpring. Our goal is to depart from this place called Tiredness and to overcome it, arriving at the place of Satisfaction. On our flight, you will see how I take you through the I.C.E. concept from departure to arrival, so you can go through the necessary transitions that must take place in order for you to release your energy, creating an inexhaustible WellSpring *to do* the good life.

So get on board with me. Let's board our flight and prepare to depart. Allow me to pilot you to our runway so we can take off and fly above the clouds and into a world of achievement, as we reset our lives and finally arrive at the place where we discover how to create our very own WellSpring—living energized in the land of Satisfaction.

Burn it up!

Dr. Jason Littleton

Section One

Inspiration

Unleash U: Personal Motivation

Chapter One

Unapologetically and with all forthrightness I want to talk with you. I am not focused on anyone else; in fact, right now, there is just you and I. This is good. I want to increase your awareness of yourself to open you to another perspective about doing your life.

This book is about energy in a sense, but more concretely it is about you doing your life without excuses—without the failure of overcoming limits. I want to empower you. I want you to become aware—aware of U.

What We're Made Of

You are a spirit who has a soul living in a body. For some I know that this may be hard to conceive. In fact, talking about a spirit may be quite frightening. However, it can be more frightening not understanding who you really are.

I want to go deeper in this. On the outside we see ourselves in the mirror. We see our face, our eyes, our skin color, and we think, "That's me." We see someone else's face, eyes and skin color and we think, "That's them." It's just that that's not quite true. You are the person *inside* that body. This is important to understand because it is the key to separating our control over our soul and body. Having more energy and doing more in life has everything to do with managing our soul and our body to do more things.

We've all heard the adage, "Sticks and stones may break my bones, but words will never hurt me." We have even heard people talk about how the things we hear on the radio or see in the movies do not influence our actions but that *we* influence our actions. The thinking behind this simply is incorrect. Words hurt. And they heal. They also help us to see the separation between our components. For example, when a friend says something cruel to you that hurts, where are you affected? Are you affected naturally, meaning your body? Or are you affected inside? We all know that we are affected inside, meaning our spirit and soul.

Deeper still, anyone who ever has lost a loved one, whether to separation or passing away, knows it can take time to heal. Even when in our minds (which are a part of our soul) we know that we need to move on for we have grieved for such a time, we find we cannot, because we are still hurting. What is this? This is U. Not that you are the hurt or the pain, but U are the person who appreciates the hurt; who appreciates the pain. In the same way, U are the person who appreciates the joy—who appreciates the happiness of a marriage or a celebration.

The Invaluable U

U are special. There is no one identically like U. You have to appreciate this truth. Embrace it. Knowing who you are is at the core to empowering you to overcome.

So many times, when I am counseling my patients, I try to get them to realize how important they are. Whether I am talking to an individual about their illness or about their emotional concern such as depression, I try to show them that they are not their illness. They are not their depression. Again, we are not our face, eyes or skin color. We are not our illness or depression. We are a spirit, carbon copy to no one. Unique in this way, we have something of value to add to all. And this is what I am trying to get U to see. U are important and we would miss all the creativity, innovation and talents that U have to offer.

Now that you see this, I want you to expand your thinking. What are you not thinking about? What are you not seeing? What value are you not adding? Can you identify it?

Unveiling New Energy By Discovering Our Passion

In *Runaway Bride*, Julia Roberts played the role of Maggie Carpenter, a woman who ran away from the altar every time she was about to get married. Richard Gere played the role of Ike Graham, a reporter and the eventual love interest of Maggie. Ike was attempting to answer the question as to why Maggie always stood up her would-be husband at the altar. Ike, who also was left at the altar by Maggie, later to marry her in the end, did actually discover the reason Maggie always left men at the altar. It was that she never understood what she wanted in men or in life. This was brought out in the movie when Ike pointed out to her that even when it came to how she wanted her eggs prepared, she had no idea. Thus, in the movie, we saw rather comically how Maggie took the time to discover eggs prepared different ways to find out how she actually liked them.

Like Maggie, we too have to take the time to find out more about ourselves. What value can we add? What do we actually want to do? What do we actually like? Taking the time to do this can be very intimidating, which is why I think most of us get stuck here. However, if we would put in the time that we put in to plan a wedding or a party, we would find a world of things we never knew about ourselves. Here's the key: What we find out about ourselves—our dreams, wants and the value we can add—are the very things that become our passion and our drivers in life.

Without identifying our passions in life, a vacuum is created. Instead of being filled by our dreams and goals, it is filled by dissatisfaction, lack of motivation and soon, depression. I have found that a lot of times we can feel tired, fatigued and bored because we are not moved to do anything. This can be a dangerous place to be. Here, I have even counseled patients who thought of ending it all. Don't get me wrong—chemical imbalances are a part of what we call clinical depression, and still having something that moves you in life can be your saving grace.

What we find out about ourselves—our dreams, wants and the value we can add—are the very things that become our passion and our drivers in life.

U are a person we need. We need U to unleash U. We need U to identify your drive in life; to discover your dreams, wants and desires. We need U to do them so we can be enriched. You see, if you'll take on the attitude that says, "I have a responsibility *to do* my life," then you'll have something to live for. Having something to live for is everything because it can be the driving force to move you to act tired or not.

Sometimes in my clinic patients will tell me, "I'm so depressed" or "I'm so tired that I cannot even get out of bed." Often I think to myself—and even, sometimes I use as an example—that if one would recognize what is important to them, they would be moved into action. One extreme example I'll occasionally give to the right patient is that if your son or daughter were drowning in your pool, no matter how depressed or tired you were, you would be moved to save them. I know this is an extreme graphic example, but it is one that proves that depending on the gravity of the matter, you will take action no matter how you feel.

If you place more gravity on your goals in life, you'll find that you will overcome the very hindrances that bind you. You'll get up and do—no matter what. Friend, I want you to be so filled with the knowledge of who you truly are and what you truly want in life that you are always moved *to do*.

Chapter Two

Words are underestimated, yet one of the most powerful and readily available anecdotes to improving our lives. Words convey not only the energy contained within the frequency of sound, but also, they convey the power of intent and meaning, which inspirits us and touches the heart of our souls. But not just that, words have put men into action; they have rallied the bodies of men—fighting men—into the darkest of nights, and even moved them to march straight into known on-point gunfire, having not mistaken the moment for anything less than impending death.

Words: Underestimated—yes. Unable—no. My friend, without being heavy-handed, I want to present before you now the very thing—that is, if you choose your words right—that can turn your world around and launch your life into a universe of possibility, reality and ultimate personal victory.

Hear me as clear as day: There are *words of life* and there are words that improve life. Also there are *words of death and demise* and there are words that destroy life. Recognizing and accepting words of life must come from a revealed understanding of the benefits such words provide. Find them and your life will be changed forever.

Positively Speaking Our Way to an Effervescent Life

Whenever I am working with a patient, motivating them to improve their life—to live better—I always teach them to say positive things about themselves and their outcome. I empower them by speaking words to them that improve their life; sometimes words of life. I want to strengthen their spirit—strengthen them. For remember, you are a spirit with a soul in a body (Chapter One). Thus, I constantly prove the old adage wrong about "sticks and stones" because when I encourage patients with what I call the most healing type of medicine around—words—I actually lift their spirits. But not just that, I touch their soul. When I am counseling, my words used to instruct can actually help change the way my patients think or see their world.

Sometimes as a physician, I have an opportunity—a window—during the 15-minute encounter to begin to heal a lifetime of hurt. This is one of the most sacred things I hold in all earnestness when it comes to patient care—my responsibility to hold a person's private world in all confidentiality. As a family physician, surgically, I will begin to listen, and then cut out damaging word pictures left inside a person's heart with words that improve their life. This is compassionate care. On one hand, I could just be empathetic and tell them how difficult their circumstance is; tell them brighter days are coming, then listen to their heart, lungs, place a psych referral, prescribe an antidepressant and walk out the door. Or instead, I can take some time to look them in the eye, hear them out and reinforce—even if briefly—their ability as a human being to overcome situations and circumstances in life. I find that the latter option is the better option.

Or instead, I can take some time to look them in the eye, hear them out, and reinforce—even if briefly—their ability as a human being to overcome situations and circumstances in life.

Words Heal and Energize

You see, humans are spirit, and the only way to heal the human spirit is with spirit-type things—*words*. Natural things treat natural things—for instance, tangible medicines for the body—whereas spiritual things treat spiritual things, and also natural things (we'll discuss this further, here in this chapter, and also, later in the book). We've all heard the stories time and again of that comatose person whose spouse would not stop talking to them until they came to themselves. And what does the comatose person always say when they wake up? "I heard you talking to me," or "I remember something that you said."

You see, humans are spirit, and the only way to heal the human spirit is with spirit-type things—words.

Friends, words *heal*. I've discovered countless times that we humans are resilient. I've seen people who I thought wouldn't live beyond the year show up again in my office, bodies withered by sickness and disease—poor habits—who time after time continue on with their lives, a lot of times effervescent with a *to do* attitude. These types just amaze me. I mean, people who physically shouldn't be able to show up in my office do, and I think, "This has a lot to do with how they feel about themselves, what they have to live for, and their outlook on life that keeps them going." How do I know? Because I hear it in their words—their conversation. You can always predict what's around the corner for people by what they are saying. When people release words of productivity and excitement, God forbid an accident or something tragic, I usually feel confident that they are going to be around a bit. They are motivated *to do*. In essence, their words are a force of healing to their bodies—to them.

Words: Our Energy-Filled Surgical Instruments for The Conscious and Subconscious Mind

Words get into our subconscious and grow. Have you ever started singing the lyrics to a song that you heard a week ago in the mall, of which you haven't heard since that time? We all have. But why did those lyrics all of a sudden spring up? Where were they all this time? They lived in your subconscious mind, and there they matured into your conscious world. Please don't draw back when such ambiguous-seeming terms are used. Let me help.

Whenever I talk to my patients about their conscious and subconscious minds, I make it extremely tangible. Earlier, when you were driving, you know, with one hand on the steering wheel and the other holding your phone wherewith you were discussing how things went at the office—this moment, the moment before the baby fawn decided to walk about

100 feet in front of your car—you were found for the most part in your *subconscious state*. But then that fawn reminded you again that you truly do live in this conscious world, as evidenced by the gush of epinephrine that raced through your veins, giving you that pop-fizzing, tingling internal sensation in your body, which we physicians know as your fight or flight response. This shifted you into conscious thinking again, allowing you to graciously—so elegantly—maneuver your car, not hitting the unsuspecting baby deer.

That, my friend, is your conscious and subconscious. Consciously you talked on the phone, subconsciously you drove your car (see any problem with this?). At any rate, this vivid example clearly distinguishes the abutting states of mind.

What's my point? There, in your subconscious mind, lives a realm where you can do amazing things, such as drive a car. Inasmuch, the words spoken to you or by you for better or worse—life or death—can impact you in ways unimaginable to the conscious mind. Words have been planted throughout your life in your subconscious mind that germinate into your conscious world *in their time*, producing whatever was initially seeded. That is why that song you heard last week all of a sudden popped up. That is why the advertisers on the commercial buy multiple T.V. slots to motivate you *to do* or buy their product, because they know that in the right conditions their slogans—*in their time*—will grow roots in your subconscious mind, popping up all for the purpose of putting them and keeping them in the black.

Inasmuch, the words spoken to you or by you for better or worse—life or death—can impact you in ways unimaginable to the conscious mind.

But this is also why hearing words year after year from that school teacher, mistaken parent, husband or wife, which have only proved detrimental and destructive to your self-esteem and life, have never relinquished their hold on you after all this time. Such words of abasement have only matured, growing strong roots and strongholds in the subconscious mind with above-ground thorns in your conscious environment—shackling your life;

threatening your potential.

Words Overcome, Uplift and Energetically Inspirit Us

But with a word, one can pull up all the weeds that have unearthed your joy. Sometimes, it may take repeated words over time. This is why I say it does no good to *only* be empathetic to patients and ballyhoo dollar-backed promises. I have to *speak* to the core of the issue. *Speak to them.* Be honest. Be personal. Speak *life* to their spirit. It will get into their soul, entering into their subconscious mind and changing their conscious life.

I like that scene from *Good Will Hunting* where Will Hunting (Matt Damon), at the climax of the movie, interfaces with Sean Maguire (Robin Williams) in his office. In this ending scene, Will is at his breaking point, where—yet to disclose the years of hurt that he has weathered around all his life—he starts to let down his seemingly impervious shield, protecting obvious wounds he had inside all at Sean's words—*"It's not your fault."*

Friend, maybe you need to hear that today, after all the things *they* have said about you; all the things you have heard throughout your life that have left a damaging image in your spirit and a nutrient-barren subconscious mind. Maybe you need me to say to you, "It's not your fault." But maybe—and let me empower you by this—you need to hear yourself say, "It's not *my* fault."

I want you to know today that you can speak words to yourself that improve your life. You can unearth the most hardy-rooted words that seem to embed themselves as far down as Hell and that have been seeded as far back as you can remember, all by speaking words to yourself that promote a brighter future—a brighter outcome. Speak good things about yourself. Use encouraging words—and if you catch sight of, use *words of life*.

Chapter Three

Dreaming Above the Clouds

I have wanted to write this chapter for years. And now … I'm finally writing it. All my life, I've been a big fan of dreaming—going beyond my present place. Dreaming has always given me something to look forward to in life. In essence, this book was once a dream. And now it's a dream-reality.

Dreaming is a part of life. In the introduction, I briefly talked about the components of man. Man is a spirit with a soul in a body. When it comes to dreaming, the second part of man is highlighted—the soul. The soul is composed of the mind, will, emotions, intellect and imagination. It is our imagination that becomes front and center when we dream.

James Pierce, Ph.D, is known for saying that the imagination is the canvas of our minds. When I think of a canvas, I personally don't think about a surface of a painting—though that is what a canvas is used for. Instead, I think about something a little larger, like a movie screen. Here, I am able to visualize my life on screen in motion, in the theater of my mind. Stacia Pierce, Ph.D (who is the wife of Dr. James Pierce), a renowned businesswoman and success speaker, said in her book *Pursue Your Purpose and Live Your Dreams* how our dreams can be visualized like an actual movie and played back as much as needed in order for us to grasp the coming attractions in our lives.

Here's the key: In order to grasp coming attractions, we have to first learn how to see beyond the limits of our natural eyes. Or put another way, we have to visualize the invisible. How do we do this? Simple. To visualize the invisible we must identify our borders in life and then ask ourselves the question, "What's on the other side?" Our dreaming should always be our theorized construct to that question.

Here's the key: In order to grasp coming attractions, we have to first learn how to see beyond the limits of our natural eyes. Or put another way, we have to visualize the invisible.

Dreaming Beyond the Horizon for a More Passionate and Energized Life

Christopher Columbus knew this when he first sailed across the Atlantic. He looked from the European coast of Portugal and identified his border—the horizon. Then he asked the question, "What's on the other side?" Now at this point, you have to imagine that Mr. Columbus would have at least constructed a mental image of what he thought was on the other side of the horizon. You don't assemble a crew and resources and sell the concept of sailing past the horizontal line without telling yourself and others that indeed the world is round. Let's be practical. No good salesman makes a profit selling a product that he does not first understand himself.

Moreover, in the case of Mr. Columbus, his product was intangible; for he was selling the concept that the world was a sphere and not flat. He not only had to be detailed in his sales pitch but he had to be detailed in his understanding of his intangible product, which means he had to see it for himself—he had to mentally see what was impossible at that time to see naturally. For who is willing to spend a fortune on anything from a person who cannot fully explain what they are selling? Furthermore, when you are asking a person to sail with you and buy the intangible concept that the world is a sphere, your asking price is essentially the lives of those you are selling it to.

Dreaming Over Fear To Do the Things That Move Us

Which brings up another point essential to dreaming: Dreaming takes courage. You have to first have courage to go beyond your mental horizons before you ever cross your physical ones. When we go beyond the limits of the mind, we expand our thinking to areas we have never thought before, creating a vacuum where corresponding actions soon follow. One of the reasons people do not dream is that they know they will be compelled to go there in the natural; meaning, to pioneer new physical terrain that they previously only mentally explored. This is risky business. But for me, it's the only way to truly achieve full satisfaction in life. It may be that dreaming might not require risking your life; and yet, *it may be* that dreaming does require risking your life. But you have to count up the cost. I always ask people, "Is being afraid to dream worth not living your dream?"

You have to first have courage to go beyond your mental horizons before you ever cross your physical ones.

I'm going to be honest with you. When I am in an airplane, there are times when I feel very unsettled. Being 35,000 feet in the air, with the flight totally out of my control but left in the hands of the pilot, at times can be an unsettling thought. Furthermore, when I am experiencing great turbulence, thoughts of never touching the ground again do cross my mind. But I love flying. I love being in the air. I love going somewhere new. I have told myself that when it comes to flying, whether it is domestic or foreign, I will never let the fear of flying, or even the fear of death, keep me from traveling where I want to go in life. The cost of not getting there and missing out on something new is greater than getting there. Personally, I cannot live with that. Please hear me right—I am not saying go put your life on the line, but I am saying that going and doing what you want in life is worth facing every fear that you have—even death.

Do not miss out on flying because you are afraid the plane might fall out of the sky. Do not miss going for that career change because you are afraid you will not be successful and end up without a job. Do not *not* go for what you want in life, if it's admirable, honest and true, because you are afraid of what others will think. Friends, this is your life. You have to live it. You have to truly be all that you can be and unleash all that is in you. You cannot let anyone or anything hold you back! You cannot blame others for why you did not do what you knew to do. Don't stay in bed. Don't stay inside. Get out and do your life. Chase your dreams. Go and do!

And listen: A lot of you know what your dreams are. You know you are supposed to be that doctor, that chef, that lawyer. You know you are supposed to explore the world, make that speech or go and meet someone new. You just have to stop making excuses. Stop saying to yourself, "I'll do it when this happens or that happens." Stop saying, "If it were not for so and so …" Listen, not living your dream is not worth it. Living afraid … that's not good enough for me. Go and do something now toward your dream. Identify the areas in your life where you think *I can't do this* or *I am not that*, and then go beyond that limit first in your mind so that you can go beyond that point in your natural life. Dreaming is everything.

Dreaming is everything.

Dreaming Takes Concentration

As you explore your dream life, do not only record it in your mind, record it on paper! You have to write down the vision so that you can run toward it. You have to continually see where you are going in life! Inundate yourself with your dream so that you are so consumed with it, so much so, that it is all you can think about—moving toward your destination; staying focused on what you are passionate about! This passion is the wind in your sails; the hot air in your balloon.

Moreover, dreaming takes focus. So not only do you need to write down your dream, you have to take time out to go and dream. You have to plan to dream so that you create an outlet for inspiration to rush in. This may also mean that you have to go somewhere inspiring! Setting the atmosphere is the invitation for dream thoughts to come. We all know that when we hear an inspiring speaker or see something amazing, that experience causes us to see and think something greater about our world. Seeing something greater is what we need because it reminds us that we too are made to do something great. We need that. We need to see great so that we dream great, eventually leading us to do great things.

Your Energy is in Your Dream

So what does all this have to do with overcoming tiredness? When it comes to overcoming tiredness, your dream is supposed to move you to action despite how you feel. When you have identified your true passion, you'll find that getting to your destination is more important than just staying where you are. For those who tell me all the time that they cannot get out of bed, to them I say, sit down, get a pen and paper and cross over mentally—dream yourself out of those sheets! Let that dream light a fire under your legs so unquenchable, that inspiration just rushes in and fills your life with passion that moves you, so that no tired bone in your body will stop you.

Even tiredness is a mental barrier that needs to be crossed. Tiredness is part mental. Friend, I've been there too. I have been afraid to cross that barrier—the barrier of tiredness. I have said to myself that if I cross over that line and spend all my energy, how will I pick myself up again? It's almost like we are afraid to spend our last amount because we are afraid to be stranded somewhere or to fall short. But friend, that's fear.

Even tiredness is a mental barrier that needs to be crossed.

And remember, if we are pursuing our purposeful passions, fear is not justifiable to stop us from reaching our destination. I'd rather we think, _let's exhaust all we have_, and fall on our face trying. At least we did something worth doing. The good news is, if it's worth doing, we'll be infused with motivation to finish what we've started and we'll get there even if we have to crawl.

When you are under the clouds, all you see a lot of times is gray matter in your life. No excitement. No stimuli to grow, move or pursue. Again, you have to imagine that there is a sun in your life. You have to imagine that there is better. Only then will you believe—despite the amount of times you have tried and failed to live a happier life—that there still is something greater above the clouds; something worth trying again for. Something worth figuring out, knowing that life above the clouds is a whole lot brighter and definitely more free. Not only that, but flying above the clouds is worth the ticket, no matter the cost.

Chapter Four

Until recently, I never understood the practice of connecting the dots, which we used to do in kindergarten. I thought it was a game. I thought it was nothing more than an occupation of our attention, passing the time until our parents picked us up from school. We would connect the dots to form an object—be it a car or a horse. A lot of times we would not be able to see the object until all the dots were connected; however, I remember that sometimes we would be able to see it. Moreover, now in retrospect, I see the point of that exercise.

Connecting the dots is all about goals, and goals are our dots in life that form a picture if we connect them right. Like dots, goals are our picture anchors that serve us as a point of reference, so we can navigate our dreams successfully. In my last chapter, I discussed how we can form dream pictures with our imagination. It is these pictures that are outlined by our dots in life. But here's the key: We must identify our goals in life and connect them to fully see our dream-realities come to pass. It is the fulfillment of this that helps us feel satisfied and that excites us to do more in life.

We must identify our goals in life and connect them to fully see our dream-realities come to pass.

Turning Our Dreams into Goals to Generate Energy

Dreams turn into goals when we set a deadline to do them. But we cannot afford to stop right there. We must *pursue* our goals. We must *connect* the dots. The space between dots is actually time. The time between point A and point B contains an energy differential. Now here's the key: Each connected dot increases the capacitance of your wellspring. *Capacitance* is the charged potential between two conductors. In other words, when we accomplish our goals in life, we add to our dream-reality picture, producing momentum or drive to fuel the accomplishment and pursuit of fulfilling our total life's purpose. This momentum that develops is our **wellspring**, which—through the proper cultivation of this force—provides an ongoing stream of energy that can be harvested *to do* our life.

Allow me to take the concept of a wellspring further. Waterfalls are a perfect example of a wellspring because they illustrate the example of going from a point of high energy potential (at the top of the waterfall) to one of low potential (at the bottom of the basin). When water falls, energy is transferred, just like how a current is exchanged between two conductors in regards to capacitance. Though energy is transferred, it is still not harvested until we *connect* it to something to transduce the energy potential and exchange it into a tangible resource. Thus, if we place a cylindrical wheel with paddles underneath the waterfall to capture the energy transferred, now we take the energy potential and transduce it into active work production. In this illustration, the waterfall is the everlasting generator and the paddle wheel is the transducer. The entire system is the wellspring.

Our goals in life must be the impetus to generate our energy potential. As we pursue our goals in life, we can capture the energy potential present from our passion to achieve our desired outcome and transduce it into tangible work produced, which will help us to get from point A to point B. This work that is getting done is one of the core building blocks to living our life. Along these lines, when we add the benefits of mental focus, proper nutrition, rest and exercise to the equation, we are now creating a perpetual system that—through the principle of momentum—creates an ongoing driven life, or in essence, a personal wellspring. This is the sole purpose of this book: to unleash the wellspring in your life.

Our goals in life must be the impetus to generate our energy potential.

Determination Connects Our Goals

Accomplishing goals unto the achievement of our global outcome takes determination. *Determination* is the unwillingness to lose focus on the task at hand. This in itself takes an investment of energy; however, when you realize that this investment of energy is outweighed by the energy produced through the resulting momentum of success, then the investment becomes a no-brainer. But this is where many fall off.

In my clinic, I work with a good percentage of patients who are dealing with depression and anxiety. From my experience with patients, depression and anxiety are two entities of the same coin. They are determination robbers and energy-potential busters. When a person is depressed or anxious, they lose focus on goal pursuit. This disrupts the wellspring production system. These mood disorders prevent a person from dreaming or seeing above the clouds. Again, goals come from dreams, and our goals are the things that establish our passions in accomplishing our dream-realities.

Thus, when I am treating depression and anxiety, I take a multidisciplinary approach. I use medicines as well as cognitive behavior therapy to help an individual rise above their present mood state. My goal is to have my patients dream again. I want them to remember what got them passionate long ago and then I attempt to root those passions through the creation of goals. I want to enlarge their vision again. And by doing this, I am helping to re-establish their own personal energy potential so they can be energized *to do* their life. Depression and anxiety are a source of fatigue. Do not mistake them for anything less. They will drain you and cause you to feel like not accomplishing anything. Depression and anxiety are a reason why people are tired and have low energy.

Eat a Carrot

To increase motivation in life when it comes to overcoming the mood disorders of depression and anxiety, I tell my patients to go and eat a carrot. Not literally—though eating carrots is a natural source of fuel that will help establish physical energy (we'll talk more about this in the Execution section)—but I tell them to put a carrot in front of them in the form of a motivating reward. We've all seen the cartoon of a horse being motivated to push forward in pursuit of eating the carrot on the end of the stick. Well, in the same way, I tell my patients that you have to put a reward out there in front of you so that you are driven to go forward. You have to press forward unto your goals for a prize to be obtained.

There's simply no fun in arriving to a place without receiving something desirable. Come on—no one looks forward to doing anything without some sort of reward, praise or accomplishment. I mean, we all go to work for the goal of receiving a paycheck, right? In the same way, I tell my patients to identify the reward connected to their goal so that they can run toward it.

You may be that person who is tired because of anxiety or depression. You may be the one who is not motivated or excited to push forward. Friend, today I want to communicate that you can begin again. Your dreams are just on the other side of your clouding day. Your goals just have to be realized again. Don't stop believing that you will be a success. You do not have to feel discouraged that your dreams will ever become reality because of missed opportunities or failed attempts. Failed attempts are just a form of eliminating unprofitable methods, helping us to whittle down to profitable ones. We have to look at it this way. You have to know that your energy is contained in the pursuit of your goals and your wellspring is unleashed in connecting the dots to fulfill your overall purpose. You can refocus again!

You have to know that your energy is contained in the pursuit of your goals and your wellspring is unleashed in connecting the dots to fulfill your overall purpose.

You Can Break Bad Habits and Have More Energy To Do the Good Life

Furthermore, you can break bad habits. Sometimes our bad habits drain us from profitable energy. In our attempts to break bad habits, sometimes discouragement sets in as a result of getting stuck in a rut. Have you ever been there? You know when you get in an insane cycle of "here we go again"—your effort is not translating to purposeful gain. Have you ever tried to do your 'to do' list, getting to the end of your day and not accomplishing what you really set out to do? You say to yourself, "I'll complete it tomorrow," but when tomorrow comes you still find yourself falling short because either something came up or you just were so drained that you could not get off the couch.

I've been there. This can be one of the most self-defeating feelings. But I want you to know that if we will take our goals on our 'to do' list and fractionate them into smaller steps, we'll find that we will be able to swallow them more easily. I call this the *Littleton Principle*—taking our goals and fractionating them (making them *little*) in order to accomplish the bigger picture (make a *ton* of difference). When you get stuck in a rut in accomplishing your goals, remember to fractionate them. You'll find you'll get more done with less energy than going nowhere with maximum energy. It's like riding a 21-speed bicycle uphill. If you switch into a lower gear, you may be taking less ground, but you are still moving forward in a manageable way with less effort; as opposed to cycling the same terrain in high gear and exhausting every ounce of your energy without satisfactory gain.

When you get stuck in a rut in accomplishing your goals, remember to fractionate them.

So much of having more energy in life and overcoming tiredness is maintaining our bounce—maintaining our momentum. When we fail or are disappointed in life, we often *feel* down and out. Point blank ... something can shake us to our core. It's not just our emotions and mood that must be managed here; we must also be mindful of our energy. I have observed that a lot of my patients who have depression and anxiety often feel a sense of chronic fatigue. I have found that you can live with a mood disorder for so long that you do not realize the energy you used to have. But one thing's for sure: You know you lack that extra oomph to get things done.

Having a setback can also swerve your energy by skewing your drive—your routine momentum. You have to protect this. You have to realize that as we focus on our goals in life, there are going to be things that confront us. We will have headwinds, waves and turbulence. It's to be expected. When it comes and causes a delay, we must decide for the sake of protecting our mood—for the sake of protecting our dreams and goals—and for the sake of protecting our drive, momentum and *energy*, that we will be determined to get to our destination. That we will realize once again that we have something inside us that others must benefit from. That we can use our words and affect our life.

We have to remember that if we must enlarge our vision and dream above the clouds, we can then see what we can achieve by turning our visions into goals. And it's our goals that keep us hungry. It's our goals that help us to put one step in front of the other, letting us know even when we are down that there's something left on our plate—there's something left unfinished. And even in our darkest days we'll notice that we still have that unction, that flame, to get back up and finish no matter what.

Friends, we have taken off and are now in the air flying high. I have shown you the importance of U. I have discussed with you the power of words. We have dreamed above the clouds and grabbed our vision to produce goals. Now I want to leave you with this: an action step. As we climb higher and higher in our flight, I want you to fuel yourself, your dreams and even others around you by speaking strong words to your situation, stating your desired end result. To you who have no energy, say, "I am more energized every day in every way." To you who cannot see above the clouds, say, "I am enlarging my vision and seeing more today than ever before." And to you who feel down and out, say, "I will rise again no matter what and no matter how hard this is." You must speak these words in your hurt—in your pain—*and especially*, in your most un-energized, darkest hour.

This is the beginning to overcoming tiredness. As we go on, I'll discuss with you in the next section how to mentally prepare to have more energy, and in the last section we'll discuss physical actions and nutritional goals to help you enjoy more energy in your life. But realize this: I cannot get you to have more energy if you do not understand the inspirational aspect of your health. When we negate our spirits, we then get back into fads and get-energy-quick schemes that fade quickly and are not in it for the long haul. Sure, I can tell you to drink this, eat that, do this, but if you have no goals, no plans—or even if you are just down and out—what good will a few tips do for you? So get comfortable and enjoy this flight because I am interested in you—the total U. And we *will* get to our destination.

Section Two

Concentration

Clear Thinking: Flying Above the Negative with Positive Thinking

Chapter Five

STOP. Go no farther because this is a clean slate. We cannot afford to take another step thinking the same way. We have pushed over the chess pieces in the energy game we were losing and set them up again. We have reset the score back to zero and started a new game. We have been given another chance to do something new—something different. But before we move I want to tell you something. I'd like to tell you that if we do not rethink this we will undoubtedly produce the same thing. We will rehearse the same steps. We will face the same defeating fatigue. Before we move—before we *execute*—I want to brainwash you. I want to retrain the way you think. I want to string together words that you will read—and think—in order to do your life. And *to do* your life means to *achieve*—and nothing less than that.

Routines that Refuel

*The Energy Secrets **To Do** the Good Life* is the subtitle of this book. In order to achieve with high energy, we must put our routines (first we must have routines) before us—to benefit us—so that we create a WellSpring and do our lives with an ongoing, reproducible supply of energy that we can draw on in order *to do*. That is the thesis, the core and the purpose of this book.

You already know that the way you were feeling was not good enough. You already understand that you need to change or the same thing will happen. Change is not just something different, for you can just participate in another fad if that were the case. Change is supposed to be permanent to better your life.

The way we think determines where we go in life. It determines what we do. Anything that determines going somewhere takes energy. Thinking takes energy. If we take the perspective of ourselves as a volume of energy that is poured out when we do things in life, giving our all in life or in any given day can be depressing—or better yet, tiring. Once we're poured out—that's it! That's the old way of thinking. Reset. Now think this way: We are not just a volume of energy, we are a channel, allowing energy currency to be exchanged. Everything in life has a flow. We cannot survive without one. This book is designed to help you create that flow, or WellSpring, in your life.

Everything in life has a flow.

WellSpring is a routine; but much more than that—it is a way of thinking. When I think of the concept of a wellspring, I think of a whirlpool or vortex that continually thrives off of the swirling momentum, producing greater undertow. I want your life to be constructed in a way that everything you do—your schedule, your nutrition, your rest—is circled around making and keeping you productive *to do* life.

Mental energy is a big part of creating a cyclone of energy in your life. When we look at our day and do not connect the dots of each activity that we have to do in that day—understanding why it's important to excel in them—we lose the power of motivation in that day. When we lose our motivation for our daily tasks, then we are unenthused and it becomes difficult to stay energized. For example, a lot of times people look at their jobs in this way. When they first applied for their job, they could not wait to start work because now they had secured a source of income and had a place to belong. After some time, some people see waking up in the morning and going to work as a drag. They are unenthused and tire quickly.

Take that same day and put an exciting event later in the evening—like a party, for instance—and then all of a sudden, most people get their energy back. Why? The reason is because going to a party is seen as fun and engaging (just like how their job initially was) and what was taken as physical tiredness all of a sudden becomes recharged. The point here is that it was not physical fatigue—it was mental fatigue. Mentally you can lose your energy by losing your excitement for things in life. In the example, mental energy was lost by not seeing the significance of daily work on the job as engaging anymore.

Remember, you must connect the dots in life to see the entire picture. If you will see your work as something that you put yourself into to add value to your employer, to yourself, to your community, then you will be able to regain its significance to you in life. This will help you stay motivated, nurturing and bolstering your mental energy. In a way, your mental energy depends on your daily perspective. If you are one of those T.G.I.F. (Thank God It's Friday) people, then the rest of the week is horrible for you. If this is you (be honest), then you lack the right perspective to stay energized through each day, because you have more of a survive-the-day mentality instead of a thrive-today mentality. So it won't matter if I tell you to eat more blueberries, get seven to nine hours of sleep or perform this exercise, because your perspective is totally off. Can you see now why I must use the I.C.E (Inspiration - Concentration - Execution) concept to teach you how to have more energy?

If you will see your work as something that you put yourself into to add value to your employer, to yourself, to your community, then you will be able to regain its significance to you in life.

Letting Go of Things That Mentally Weigh Us Down and Cause Us to be Tired

To have more mental energy, you must relieve yourself of things that weigh down your mind. Worry, anxiety, fear and lack of focus all weigh down the mind. Why? Again, these things steal your excitement for the things in life. Stolen excitement = lack of motivation. Sometimes in life we can be so used to worrying and being anxious that we develop a subconscious pattern of thinking this way, without being aware of it. In essence, we have developed a WellSpring of worry and anxiety instead of peace, joy and energy. You can help break these destructive energy habits by using the Littleton Principle of fractionating to break down your elephant concerns, and critically thinking about how another approach can be more constructive. This is how we allow our minds to rest. When we let go of destructive thinking, we find that we have now entered a void where a sense of anxiety can actually overtake us, because now we have come into a new mental place that we are not used to—a mind free of being weighed down.

In this place, if we do not act quickly to replace constructive thinking where we used to think destructively, we will revert back to our old thinking. We must become comfortable with thinking positive and letting go of life's concerns in order to rest. When we do, we will find that we'll have more energy. Letting the mind rest of destructive thinking by going for a walk, listening to music, exercising, praying—being still—will help us to Reset so we can think clearly and engage in a life of more energy by having more mental energy.

The *will* is a component of our soul (remember the soul encompasses the mind, *will*, intellect, imagination and emotions). The will is the component of our soul that we use to set our determination in the things of life. "I will do this. I will do that." Our will is the setting in us that sets the direction for what we are going to do. Our attitude in life depends on how we *will* it to be set. This is important to having more energy because it determines our outlook for our life—for each day. So if we will to have the attitude that says, "Though I do not feel like going to work today, I am going to go—in fact, I will go to work giving all I have, being an asset on my job." That attitude is not looking to survive; instead, it's looking to *thrive today.*

The person who wills their attitude to take this perspective will be able to fly over destructive thinking and the happenstance things that can vanquish our momentum, thus draining our energy. Dr. James Pierce says that attitude determines your altitude; thus, when it comes to flying it's obvious that the attitude is essential to getting far in life. Therefore, friend, I want you to think about your attitude. No more "I can't wait till I get through the day." No. Instead think, *I am going to give all I have today because I am getting closer to completing the bigger picture for my life!*

To have more mental energy, you must relieve yourself of things that weigh down your mind.

Another component of our soul is our emotions. This is a huge one for some because some are moved by their emotions instead of their goals. Emotions are exhibited through our feelings. So if we don't *feel* like doing something, then most of the time we won't, if we fall into this category. But don't let me give you the wrong impression. Emotions are powerful and very important. They help put the color into our life and into our day. They help add to the cyclone effect, which makes our WellSpring effective toward energizing our lives. I am asking us in essence to grab hold of the wind—to capture it, and use it to our benefit.

That's what windmills do. They capture the wind and use it to transduce wind energy into a useful format to do work. And I am asking the same of each of us: to capture our emotions and transduce them to be more productive instead of letting them add to a destructive pattern of thinking—moving us to and fro, wasting our mental energy. Let's capture our emotions by concentrating our thinking and letting our feelings revolve around constructive thoughts, not destructive thoughts.

Having Energy No Matter What You Face

When we talk about flying in life or when we talk about airplanes, dealing with the wind is very important. In flight there will be tailwinds (winds that speed up planes) and headwinds (winds that slow down planes). The headwinds are what I want to deal with here because they are the type of winds that can tend to be more limiting when it comes to arriving to a desired destination on time. When a plane faces a headwind, not only will it take longer to arrive somewhere, it may face turbulence. Turbulence can be very unsettling for passengers, but pilots know it's just a part of flying. But I can see how the turbulence in life can get a person off course. You see friend, when you face turbulence in achieving your goals in life, it is crucial that you take the mindset that *my mind is fixed; focused on my destination (or goals) and I am not going to waver or get off course, no matter how long it takes.*

You have to set your will in order to do this type of flying in life. You have to channel your emotions so they do not bring you down. You can crash in life if you allow yourself. But don't allow yourself. Say, "No matter how hard this is or how long this takes, I am going to thrive in whatever I am doing today. I am going to win in life." This attitude or type of thinking is energy-protecting and energy-transducing. Thus when Monday comes, don't think, *man, if I can just get through today and make it to Friday.* No—instead, *T.G.I.M. (Thank God It's Monday) because I am going to produce something today for my employer—for my neighbor—for myself—that is going to take everyone to the next level!* Reset your thinking and you'll Reset your life by having renewed energy *to do* your life!

Chapter Six

"You know what you gotta do ... do it. ... Do it!" During the years, this phrase has meant so much to me. At times it has meant to stand strong when I had a lot to do. Sometimes it meant to work harder. Now, it means to me I *know* what I have to do. Knowing what I have to do is the preliminary to doing what I know. *Now thinking* encapsulates just that—knowing.

The preceding quotation is from one of my favorite movies of all time: *Rocky IV*. In that scene, Duke (Rocky's trainer) says those words to Rocky the night before he starts training in Russia for his Cold War fight against Ivan Drago. Here, Duke is trying to encourage Rocky to do what he knows to do, though he faces great odds. Previously in the film, Drago killed Rocky's best friend Apollo in the ring during an exhibition bout. So here, Duke is telling Rocky to train only in the way where victory is the only possible outcome, no matter what—no matter the pain.

This is now thinking: Thinking that translates to guaranteed results if you do what you know. But again, I want to point out that Rocky knew what he had to do.

To be honest with you, right here, right now is where I am. I am reminding myself of my own concept. In life, I've found that we can stall out at times. Not that we use this as an excuse, but we recognize a stall-out and work the mechanical solution. In flying, even planes—unfortunately—can stall out. But do they just immediately fall from the sky? No—they glide for a while. Fortunately, we too, glide for a while. While gliding, work the mechanical solution to get your mental engine running again. Get back into now.

While gliding, work the mechanical solution to get your mental engine running again. Get back into now.

Living in the Moment: That's Where Your Energy Is

We stall out usually because we are fixated on past occurrences for too long. Instead of thinking about the past in order to learn from it, we dwell on the past and think only of alternative *outcomes* (should have, could have, would have) instead of alternative *solutions*. So what happens is we try again. But trying again is simply not enough because we failed to RESET, or in this instance, we failed to learn from our failure, and so we return to our mistake.

Locate yourself. You're stuck in a rut. Eventually what happens is that we become so *tired* of trying, that even the thought of trying is tiring. And this type of thinking is just that: tiring. This is the epitome, the essence, of mental tiredness. Friends, this is another reason why you actually are tired. If you'll admit it, you are tired because you will not move on to what is next in your life. You don't know "… what you gotta do." You are sick and tired of being sick and tired. Hopeless is how you feel. What you feel like doing is taking a nap, because you think, "If I just rest for thirty minutes, then I'll be recharged to do my (planning/work/or just stuff)." Again, most of you do not know what is next. And so it's hard to "Do it!"

I understand. I have been there. And actually, I am there now. But I know what to do. So I am reminding myself of the concept of Now Thinking. The concept of now thinking is simply this: know what you have to do and do what you know to do. That's it … it's that simple.

The concept of now thinking is simply this: know what you have to do and do what you know to do.

Your Daily Plan is the Place Your Energy Resides

First know what you have to do, or in other words, have a plan. You should take time to write out a weekly plan or schedule. Put all the things that you routinely do in your schedule, like your morning routine, your job, activities, relaxation and personal growth actions. When you do this, remember to leave reasonable time in between each "to do" on your weekly schedule so you give yourself time to transition into each task.

For example, if you have to be at work at 8:00 a.m., don't plan to wake up at 7:30 because you leave yourself no time to drive to work; you leave no time to even shower, dress or eat, or—here's an idea—to review your to-dos for the day. To-dos are really daily tasks. Now, there are weekly tasks, or to-dos, but for all purposes of my emphasis, I am more or less focusing their meaning on daily tasks. The reason I do this is because your daily to-dos are the building blocks and essential elements to your habitual success in life. And in terms of your energy, your daily to-dos are the mainspring to your wellspring, causing you to have an energized, driven life.

Your daily to-dos come from the foundation of your weekly schedule. If you'll make your to-do list the night before (during your meditation time— we'll get to that later in this section), the next morning before you really get going, you can review it in order to concentrate further on exactly what you must accomplish in that day. Leave nothing to chance here. List the things you must do for tomorrow one by one so you clearly become aware, recognize and *know* what you must do in that day. This is how you get things done. And when it comes to breaking out of a rut, the process of planning out your next day seeps into your subconscious, allowing you to help reprogram yourself so you no longer do what you usually do, but now you do what you have never done.

Plan your next day tonight and then do what you know to do tomorrow. The awesome thing is that when you practice this, more inspiration floods in *to do* your day on another level. And the feeling of this inspiration that floods in—the feeling of energy—is the opposite of the exasperation that once flooded out, giving you that tired feeling disguised as tiredness of the mind. The inspiration that floods in presents itself only because you created a vacuum of thought, so to speak. You have removed all the cluttered stuff in your thought and organizational life, so now the inspiration that was always there floods in.

Tangibly speaking, think about hoarders and how they think. Their homes are all cluttered and messy and they are unable to function optimally. They are often uninspired, tired and depressed. Not just that, they are more likely to be obese because they are less active, given their inability to move around their own space. If they don't learn from their mistake and RESET, you could remove all their clutter and they would just create it again. Instead, they must get into the *now* and substitute their old thinking for new, organized thoughts. When they do, what will rush in is a vision of how productive and well-off they can be when the clutter is removed.

And when you create a mental vacuum, guess what follows: a physical vacuum (and I mean literally in this case)—and now, the hoarder can vacuum up all his mess. This is the antecedent, the nucleus and the entire premise of creating a WellSpring in your life—getting rid of antiquated habits that tire you out and substituting them for new, healthy life routines that propel and excel your life. Over time, these new routines should become habitual, allowing you to master what you do and gain momentum.

This is the antecedent, the nucleus and the entire premise of creating a WellSpring in your life—getting rid of antiquated habits that tire you out and substituting them for new, healthy life routines that propel and excel your life.

But don't just stop here. Step back and look at your life globally. Remember the dreams and goals we discussed in Section One? The ones you identified and wrote down? The things that were always in you that only needed to be unleashed? Yes, *those* dreams and goals. Now use them to make sure your daily to-dos are adding up to make weekly sense, and your weeks are adding up to make yearly sense, and your years are adding up to make … are U connecting the dots? Do you get the picture? When we add all this together we are making the concept of wellspring work for us, providing us the energy we need through the medium of a vacuum created by organized thinking and routine living. In Section Three, I'll show you how to bring the bodily or physical energy aspect together with this so that all cylinders are working together, so you can operate in your complete WellSpring in order *to do* your life.

Burn Your Energy Or It Will Burn You Out

Now that you know what you have to do, do what you know to do. This is the second part of the concept of Now Thinking. Now that you can see the vision of what you have to do with your mind's eye, you can do the vision with clarity. You have cleared all the entanglements that bind and prevent you mentally from concentrating and doing your goals. Though knowing what you must do does not eliminate obstacles or delete the opportunity to make excuses, it illuminates the path mentally that guarantees success every time—if you do it. Knowing what you must do helps clean out the time-wasting, slothful excuses that are akin to the unfocused, dull mind. Now things are streamlined. Now all you must do is execute—no matter what.

Friend, you can think in the now. You can get up and try again with new thinking—Now Thinking—so that you can succeed in life. I want you to learn from your mistakes instead of dwell on them. I want you to try again with a new perspective—a new attitude. Don't get depressed. Instead, enlarge your vision. See yourself getting through. Substitute your old ways with new ways and go at things again. See yourself driven. See yourself energized. See yourself doing it. When you feel stuck in a rut, like I did, remember the concept—the concept of Now Thinking. Don't go to sleep. Don't take that nap (because the truth is, you won't wake up until tomorrow or until it's too late). Instead *know*. Know what you must do and do what you know to do. Remember Rocky. Remember Duke. "You know what you gotta do ... do it. ... Do it!"

Chapter Seven

Think Again

I believe this is one of the most important chapters in this book. The reason I say this is because so far, I have provided you with tools to energize your life, but this chapter is vital because here I am going to teach you how to use those tools. Thinking is everything. It takes energy, and frankly, it's hard work. Unfortunately, it's the work part that causes most to not enter into the thinking habit on a regular basis.

I have to tell you that there is a difference between mental consciousness or awareness (passive thinking) and on-purpose processing (active thinking). To be honest, I do not consider mental consciousness or awareness to be thinking at all, but for the sake of my example, I will refer to it in this chapter and the rest of the book as passive thinking. Active thinking is concentrating and processing material on purpose with a profitable end. Most of us by default are mentally conscious—this doesn't take much; in fact, it is passive and works off our maintenance energy. You know—the energy that is just there to keep our vital organs alive.

Active thinking is concentrating and processing material on purpose with a profitable end.

Active Thinking: The Art That Energizes Us and Motivates Us to Act

Active thinking takes our inner self that we unleashed into dreams and whittled into goals--and finally processes it into an organized workflow that we can physically do. It's all active—not passive.

When we think, we ponder. Another word for ponder is *meditate*. Dr. James Pierce said it best when he said, "Meditation is visualizing, verbalizing and memorizing." A successful entrepreneur known nationwide, he teaches leaders how to think. He focuses on showing people how to crystallize their goals by writing them down on paper time and again. This is a habit I have practiced for years to focus myself and to start the process of active thinking.

Along with this, I have also learned that one needs a place and a time to think. Dr. Pierce's wife, Stacia Pierce, known as the number one Millionaire Maker, teaches her clients that you must block out time to work on your business; to think; to plan; to write. She teaches people to get into an environment where they can be productive. I have found that this is what is needed to sharpen the mind for your daily tasks. It is the unsharpened mind that fails to equip you with the mental energy required to feel physically energetic.

In family medicine, when I treat cholesterol, hypertension, obesity— even smoking cessation—I often start with the fundamental practice of encouraging lifestyle modification or habit change. There's no pharmaceutical medicine involved in lifestyle modification; instead, it involves thinking and acting differently. Here's where people struggle. I can say, "You need to exercise and eat differently to improve your cholesterol or blood pressure." You can hear and understand me. In fact, you can be super motivated to run out of my office right now and buy blueberries and use your credit card to buy new exercise equipment. You may even do that. You might take it one step farther and even exercise. "Great," you think. "I've changed!"

I wish it were that easy. Did you do something different? Yes. Did you think something different? Yes. Did you change your thinking? Unfortunately— no. Previously, I told you that you are a spirit possessing a soul in a body. You, the spirit, wanted to change in the above example. Your soul (mind, will, intellect, emotions and imagination), acting off of emotion from being told you needed to change, was the impetus to process the action. Your body executed it, buying the blueberries, exercise equipment and finally, exercising. The problem is that your emotions are not enough to sustain your continued lifestyle modification.

Programming Ourselves to Have More Energy

In Chapter Two, I illustrated the difference between our conscious and subconscious; here in this section I will elaborate on it more so as to make it more tangible and personal for you. In my last example, I painted a picture of someone acting off of their conscious efforts. None of their actions were automatic. Everything was non-programmed. Programming ourselves involves *willful*, conscious effort built on the platform of our mind and not our emotions. Concentration is the key. We must practice concentrating on what we are willing to change over and over again to make it a subconscious or automatic habit. This is active thinking or meditating.

We must practice concentrating on what we are willing to change over and over again to make it a subconscious or automatic habit.

Let me give you another colorful example. When you were 16 and learned to drive, you concentrated on the road, the steering wheel (hands in the 10:00 and 2:00 position), the driver next to you and your speed. You may even have been slightly nervous. You didn't talk on the phone or text while driving—instead you focused because you were new. Five years later, you probably realized that you do none of those things a beginner driver does. Today, you can eat, text and steer with one hand while driving—you're an expert! Unfortunately, what happens here is that what was once conscious becomes subconscious or routine. It's just that in the above example you worked in the bad habits that either you passively accepted from T.V., a parent or other mentor. These bad habits also became subconscious and automatic. You didn't realize it but you began to practice them over time.

In order to reverse this, you have to *think again*. You have to practice thinking consciously, and on purpose choose to think through the right changes over and over to drum them into your subconscious hard drive.

This is active thinking. This is meditating. You do this by visualizing, verbalizing and memorizing the steps.

Programming ourselves involves* willful, *conscious effort built on the platform of our mind and not our emotions. Concentration is the key.

OK, so you want more energy? Let's meditate this out. First, visualize! See yourself reviewing your daily plan, which you previously made (as discussed in the last chapter). This time instead of your current habitual/subconscious habit of getting to work five minutes late, hair all out of sorts, fumbling in, see yourself in your mind waking up ahead of time and smoothly preparing for your daily transition into your job (since you crystallized this on paper already, this is easy, because you are reviewing your schedule or *to do* list).

Next, see yourself at your desk and ready to work at 8:00, and not still getting your cup of coffee (we'll talk about coffee in Section Three), fixing your hair, checking your email or even your social media sites. Furthermore, see yourself *actually* working. Doing what you do. Being productive. Don't see yourself stopping at the water cooler or getting into that outside conversation. Don't see yourself paying your bills at work or daydreaming about 5 p.m. See yourself executing and doing what you said you would do when you were hired.

After work, see yourself still being productive. Don't throttle down! Keep the engines turning. We are in mid-flight. See yourself leaving work and going to the gym or taking a walk. See yourself doing your reading or your personal business. See yourself planning out the next day and taking time out to do your self-growth routines! Don't see yourself hitting the couch with chips. Don't see yourself picking up the phone and seeing how everyone else is doing (there is nothing wrong with this, but if you need energy—if you need money—then why don't you do something else; something more productive?). Don't see yourself taking a nap (you turned off the engines—you won't wake up until tomorrow).

Finally, at the end of your day, as you are truly throttling down the engines, see yourself planning tomorrow's *to-dos*. See yourself doing what we are doing now—meditating. See yourself preparing your food for tomorrow and laying out your clothes. See yourself getting deep sleep. See yourself waking up on time without hitting snooze! Do not go to bed without meditating on your next day. This is where the power of having an energized life comes from: nighttime meditation.

Secondly, verbalize! Say to yourself aloud what you will do. The act of speaking your commitments reminds you what you vowed to do, locking you in to accomplishing your *to-dos*. Words speak the language of the subconscious mind. They get into your mind and take root, reminding you of what you're supposed to do. Your words move you. Never say "I'm tired," even if you are. Instead say, "I'm energized to do what I must do today. Today, more and more energy is coming my way." The act of speaking changes your perspective. It changes your habits. You know this works— this is the same methodology that all the stores and commercials use to get you to buy their products. They *subconsciously* get into your mind to make you think that your desire to buy their product came from you.

Now, be your own commercial and plant your own desire to buy the change you want: *I'm always energized. I'm always productive. I always get the job done. I'm getting better and better today—healthier and healthier in every way. I will exercise today. I will stay on my diet. I will not overeat. I will not hit the couch as soon as I get home. No, I'm not catching a cold today. I'm staying healthy … I'm staying energized. Today is my day. I'm not taking a sick day today. I'm about to get work done today.* Friends, this is how you use your words to change your health through the process of meditation.

Lastly, memorize! In other words … step number three: Go back and learn steps one and two. Rehearse the steps we talked about. Rehearse the visualizing and verbalizing so that it becomes automatic. This takes practice, but this is how it is done. Don't be taken aback or discouraged here as you work to program your lifestyle change. You may find that it takes time and fortitude to form a habit. And guess what … it does! But also remember, it took time to form your bad habit. It's been said that it takes 21 days of consistent effort to form a habit. I'll buy that, saying this: If your habit is not formed on day 22, then keep pressing. Keep working as you drum in your new routines, being mindful that you are making headway. This is where the rubber meets the road. Practice! Practice! Practice! You can change your habits!

If You'll Meditate, You'll Have More Energy

You'll find that when you think through your life, mental clarity will enter in. You'll feel together. This is what you want. I told you in my introduction that you think you want more energy. You think you want the latest and greatest solution. But what you really want is a healthy you—a healthier mind, and finally a healthier body—to make it all work. Being healthy in totality is what you really crave. This is how I achieve more. I meditate. My secret is that I usually go for a walk after work to make the transition into my after-work work easier. It is important to have a place to meditate. Walking is my environment to get my mental juices flowing so that I can actively think and meditate. Also, in my office at home is another place where I critically think, plan and strategize. When I do this, I am deleting old habits and taking in new life modifications to improve my life and take me higher.

My message to you is simple: If you'll meditate, you'll have more energy. You'll feel more in control. You'll have an improved life. If you side-step this essential piece to modifying your life, you will forever find yourself lacking what it takes to take the next step in your life. If you only treat your body and never your mind, you'll always be the person who has a ceiling they cannot get above. Don't be that person. Don't be stuck in a rut. Think Again by visualizing, verbalizing and memorizing, and you'll change your life for good.

Chapter Eight

Focused to Finish

We've conversed about many things up to this point; things you probably thought had nothing to do with having more energy and not feeling tired. But understand this: I want you to never feel like you felt again. This book is a seed of information, of which you must plant into the ground of your heart and practice to be effective. Two-thirds of this book has been about Inspiration and Concentration, with the last third all about exercise and nutrition (Execution). The way I see it, the inspiration and concentration part is the soil and strong root, respectively, while the execution portion is the tree above ground—the part you see.

Again, let me be clear: The part you see—the tree—is what most people want. I understand. But I also understand that this is why most people cannot achieve their health goals or why they are mostly unsatisfied— because they tried so many things without ever obtaining serious gains or consistent momentum. The tree you see is not it. You have to develop everything—yourself, your mind and your body. For too long you have tried different energy drinks, diets and fads, only to start all over again. I understand. I have been there.

Now, as we close Section Two with "Focused to Finish," I want to update you with where we are on this flight. We are near our final destination, *The Land of Satisfaction*; but we are still in the air almost starting our initial descent with our final section, Execution. Before we appropriately throttle down and land, I want to emphasize the importance of being focused to finish—or in other words, landing the plane. There are usually two main times during a flight that a pilot consistently devotes most of his concentration: takeoff and landing. You see, when you land, you have to line things up and adjust your speed just right. Otherwise, you never truly finish your flight. The bottom line is, you can crash after coming all this way.

Crashing when it comes to our life goals, as far as health and energy is concerned, is finishing close to our goals yet never arriving at our goals. Whether we get stuck in a rut, quit or just say to ourselves, "We're close enough," this is actually not finishing. I know that some of you would be OK with this. You may think, "I need to lose weight. In fact, my goal is to lose thirty pounds. I lost twenty-five pounds. Yes!" First of all, don't get me wrong—losing 25 pounds is remarkable. Congratulations! But if your natural BMI range (we'll discuss this in Section Three) involves you losing five more pounds, don't land there. Finish!

Using Your Energy to Finish No Matter What

If I'm flying to Los Angeles from Orlando and the pilot drops me off in Las Vegas, I'm not saying to myself, "Awesome, I'm close! Only a few hundred miles to go!" No! I'm thinking, "I paid 500 dollars for a first-class ticket to L.A. and you stop here in Sin City. I want my money back!" Putting it in the terms of arriving to an actual destination brings my point home. My point? Finish! Be focused on finishing and getting to your destination.

When you have the right soil and strong root, you can support a good tree. You can finish your flight. Friend, I have good news: You can be focused to finish. You can set out to lose 30 pounds and actually lose 30 pounds. You can have more energy. You can start a health program and actually stick with it. But you have to believe it. You have to have the right inspiration and you must have proper concentration. Fads do not work. Systems, principles and laws do. In Sections One and Two, I dug up the old you and re-potted you. And now we're ready to land this plane. Now that I am finished with the introduction to this chapter, and as I begin to conclude the first two-thirds of this book, I am going to address the only two points I have left for you in Section Two, *Concentration*: Mind Expansion and Mental Investing. Stay seated and keep your safety belt on for this.

Mind Expansion: Enlarging Your Thinking for More Energy

You must expand your mind about what you can do. When it comes to having more energy, you have to get rid of the thinking that says, "After 8 p.m. I'm tired … I'm through … that's it." No. You're through when you're done—when you've completed your daily goal. And you cannot be concerned with how long you've worked, how tired you feel or where you're at. Complete the task. That's hard, you say? Like I talked about in a previous chapter, so much of your tiredness is mental. You have to expand your mind to do more. This means you have to mentally prepare or meditate (Chapter Seven) about giving it all you've got. It's only when you give all you've got that you create the vacuum we talked about, so that more inspiration, more creativity and more energy can come in. That's the WellSpring!

And you cannot be concerned with how long you've worked, how tired you feel or where you're at. Complete the task.

It's really the point of no turning back because you've exhausted so much—devoted so much to what you're doing that going back is not an option. You might as well finish. But to do this you have to expand your mind to do more than what the job takes. If your daily goals take eight hours, mentally prepare to go 16 so that if you're not done with what you need to do, your mental clock does not alarm and say, "It's quitting time." Planes and pilots know this. When they fly, they fuel their tanks enough to go there *and back* if need be. You have to do this mentally so that finishing your daily task is all you're focused on. When you do this, you will not feel as tired because you are mentally prepared for the long haul if necessary. Again simply put, you can do more but you have to think about it first.

Being focused to finish also means staying consistent during your journey, to the point of finishing. A lot of times what I see being done well is takeoff. But on day two, staying committed to our health or life goals is the kicker. Most people crash here, and I submit to you that one of the reasons is because they are not focused on finishing. They are not focused on seeing things through. Day two is always harder than day one—every time. You have to expand your thinking beyond day two, to the finish line, in order to not lose the fight, or in other words, become weary. You have to know that there will be obstacles, there will be turbulence, that anything worth doing is not going to be easy but that if you are going to get to your destination, you have mentally got to stay at the helm of this flight no matter what. Not only that, when you are coming into your new place you have to have expanded thinking to maintain your new habits so you will not retreat and take up your previous low-energy, unhealthy ways.

I told a patient in my clinic the other day that you have to have a Y. Yes a Y … like why are you doing what you are doing? You have to have a reason because if you do not have a reason to land this plane, to finish your goals (staying consistent to the end)—you won't. The patient I am talking about wanted to have more energy and lose weight. As I was telling him about his current situation, he became down and depressed. I asked him about this. His response was, "When I think about where I am and how I must go home and tell my wife about the bad news," (for I had discussed with him that he was overweight and had high blood pressure) "and how I have tried diet after diet, program after program, I feel bad." But I was also telling him good news about how we were going to finally meet his health goals and he would feel better. He was not seeing this. This gentleman needed to expand his mind and see what I saw about his health situation.

I gave him some homework along with the exercise and diet plan I instructed him to do. I told him to find out *why* he wanted to lose weight and have more energy. So he went home from the clinic and started the new exercise program I instructed him in. He sent me a text message when he had completed that day's exercise. I did not cheer him on with an encouraging reply. I only acknowledged the text, hoping he'd find his own reason to continue and make it past day two. And I'm still waiting on an answer. I want him to succeed. I'm doing my part. But my patient must do his and must have his own Y. So let me tell you what you already know: If you will not expand your mind and have your own reasons to do any one thing, you will not be focused to finish and as a result, you will not finish your flight.

Mental Investing: Your Energy Return System (ERS)

To be focused to finish, not only do you have to expand your mind but you also have to mentally invest. Mental investment is watering the seed. We talked about having good ground and strong roots, and now, you must water your seed. In other words, mentally invest. You have to inundate yourself with the landing strip. As they say, you have to keep your eyes on the prize.

Dr. Stacia Pierce continually talks about making storyboards and putting up pictures of where you want to go. She even has a tool devoted to this process, called *The Millionaire's Dream Book*. Her concept is all about being focused on finishing. It is about seeing the goal and achieving the goal. In her business seminars, she always talks about listening to and reading informative materials about what you are trying to accomplish. What she's teaching people to do is to water their seed—the thing they set out to do. When you continue to hear, see and work toward your goals, what you are actually doing is encouraging yourself to keep moving toward and looking at your final destination. In essence, you are encouraging yourself!

Your physical energy has everything to do with mentally investing in yourself. The more you stay encouraged about doing what you have to do today, the higher the chances are that you will stay motivated and focused to get it done no matter what. Let me end with this all too real and personal example: I have struggled to get things done. I cannot begin to tell you the amount of times I have woken up and started my day with high hopes and *to dos*, further being inspired with new ideas (things I couldn't wait to get home and complete when I finished seeing patients for the day—usually these ideas would come to me around 10 a.m. while working), only to get home and feel tired—uninspired to actually perform them. I would throttle down. I would say to myself, "Let me lie down for a twenty-minute power nap." All too often, I would lie down and not get up again. And if I did wake up, I would be too unfocused to finish my *to dos*. It was beginning to be day after day, week after week, month after month—and still I could not complete an entire day of *to dos*.

Your physical energy has everything to do with mentally investing in yourself.

I was always tired. I was always sluggish. I was always so close. There would be days that I would get 80 percent of my *to dos* done, but never finish. I was frustrated. Worn out. Caffeine wasn't making it any easier, nor was having more time to get my *to dos* completed. I became so uninspired about receiving inspiring thoughts (knowing that I was only going to get excited, yet fizzle out later when I was home, never completing them) that I would just sigh every time I got them. But I did not stop searching for an answer.

What I learned was this: If I would continue to mentally invest or encourage myself with informative materials, pictures and words—even my own coming out of my mouth—I would have the vital fuel to provide the zap (a.k.a *physical energy*) I needed to go home focused to finish my *to dos*. Every day is a flight for me, in essence. In the morning I take off and in the evening I land, being careful not to throttle down to land *before* arriving at my destination. I have to look at my life this way, as a flight. I have to see inspiring thoughts that come my way as a tailwind, sustaining them by continuing to encourage myself in them. I cannot let inspiration stand alone. I learned that I had to concentrate on it and finally execute.

Friend, expand your mind. Mentally invest. You can do this. You can dream, have goals and do them. You can be inspired and keep it. You can set out to have more energy and have it. Inundate yourself with the right people, places and things to stay focused. Remember to use the power of your own words—blow wind into your sail. Create your own tailwind.

Talk to yourself: "Hey, I am finishing this. I am landing the plane. If it's the last thing I do, I am going to lose the weight, finish my daily task whether I sleep or not, exercise to be healthy. I may feel tired and this may be hard, but I am going to finish my task no matter how I feel, no matter how depressed I am, no matter what doesn't go my way, and no matter what gets in my way. I am focused" (and you have to say this even if you don't feel it). "I have energy" (despite how tired you feel). "And I will finish. I can do it. I can do it. I CAN DO IT." That's how you focus to finish. Now, let's execute.

Section Three

Execution

Executive Wellness: Fueling Your Engine with High-Octane Nutrition

Chapter Nine

Ice is a form of energy matter underestimated. It is the composition of two hydrogen atoms chemically bonded to an oxygen atom, which we know as H_2O. The difference is that ice is the condensed form of H_2O, where the molecules composed of hydrogen and oxygen are tightly crystallized with other hydrogen and oxygen molecules, forming an intricate crystalline structure we know as the thing that cools things down.

Ice is a vacuum. We use it to suction all the surrounding heat energy necessary for it *to do* its temperature-reducing function. It pulls in the energy required to break its crystalline structure, raising its core temperature above 32°C, releasing individual molecules of H_2O to interact in the new, transformed liquid medium we know as water. If you boil water, raising it to a temperature of 100°C, you further cause the H_2O molecule to undergo a subsequent transformation, now releasing its atoms into the air and separating the bonds that connected the two hydrogen atoms with the oxygen.

Ice is also a transducer producer. It transduces the surrounding energy to produce a cooler climate, which is more suitable for desired functions to take place. We know it physiologically lowers temperatures, and yet it's underestimated because it's commonly not thought of as generating energy as it melts (while simultaneously attracting or taking away energy in the surround milieu), lowering the atmospheric temperature, and there be it, doing its purpose.

I.C.E., likewise, is the formula for human energetics: the assemblage of *inspiration, concentration* and *execution* crystallized together, producing the *WellSpring* axiom of absorbing available energy and transducing it *to do* life—your life.

We demand a lot of energy to do life!

Calories and the Joule

It is here that we've reached the demarcation point of this book, where the intangible is transduced into the tangible in order to execute the information that has been discussed. Here, appreciated energy is unambiguously discussed specifically in terms of measured energy. Our appreciated energy relating to the ability to overcome fatigue is a combination of our internal, mental and physical energy.

Physical energy is measured in *joules*, which is the SI (International System of Units) unit of energy measurement. One joule (J) equals approximately 0.24 gram calories, or 0.24 calories (cal). The *calorie* is another unit of energy derived from a pre-SI system of measurement. This *gram calorie* is not the Calorie (Calorie with the capital C refers to the *food calorie*) you and I often speak of when we discuss diet and exercise. The gram calorie refers to the *scientific calorie*. It takes approximately 1 calorie (or cal) to increase 1 gram of water by 1°C. Likewise, it takes approximately 1 Calorie (or kcal) to increase 1 kilogram of water by 1°C. Thus in essence, 1 Calorie or food calorie equals 1,000 gram calories or scientific calories. Moreover, the Calorie we think of to estimate how much food energy we receive or burn off is actually a whole lot larger than the scientific calorie. In other words, we demand a lot of energy *to do* life!

Macronutrients

The foods we eat provide us our physical energy to execute and perform our life. Food is composed of three *macronutrients* that we know as fats, carbohydrates and protein. Scientifically, we know that 1 gram of fat contains approximately 9 Calories and 1 gram of carbohydrates and proteins each contain approximately 4 Calories. Ironically, the macronutrient misconstrued and sometimes avoided the most—*fat*—provides us the most bang for our buck. Understand this: When we eat, we must include all three macronutrients in proper proportions to have a balanced diet.

Ideally, having a balanced diet is all that is necessary to living at your true BMI (Body Mass Index) range and it provides the essential macronutrients required for appropriate organ function. This is not to say that other available diets will not help you obtain your appropriate BMI; it's just keeping things in perspective. Other diets have their place and have been successful in the short term. For the long term, one wants to establish a balanced diet to nurture vital organs, keeping bodily systems functioning in top condition and in orchestration with one another.

However, as an MD, the benefit I see in short-term diet plans is to establish rapid weight loss and build momentum to motivate one to obtain a healthier BMI. Once a healthy BMI is obtained, I see it as essential to establish a balanced plan promoting overall system health. A person's level of exercise or activity must increase to substitute for short-term diet plans once completed.

In a balanced approach, a person should strive to have approximately 30 percent of his diet composed of fats, 30 percent protein and 40 percent carbohydrates. Understand that when we eat, our bodies break down food into small molecules through the process of mechanical (eating and chewing) and chemical (gastric acid and other digestive enzymatic reactions) digestion.

30% Fats

40% Carbohydrates

30% Protein

Percentages should be modified based on age, activity level, and functional purpose.

In a balanced approach, a person should strive to have approximately 30 percent of his diet composed of fats, 30 percent protein and 40 percent carbohydrates.

The percentages I presented above should be modified based on age, activity level and functional purpose. Increasing the percentage of carbohydrates, for instance, may be necessary in a vibrant 30-year-old who has an assiduous lifestyle, so his body fuels off of the easily translatable breakdown that product carbohydrates provide to fuel his brain and muscles adequately. Likewise, someone who is building muscle may want to optimize his protein calorie intake. Furthermore, people recovering from injury or illness may want to make sure their fat intake is optimized at the 30 percent approximation. Understand when I talk about fueling your body, I am inferring that you ingest elite food products in each category, giving you more bang for your buck, instead of the desserts and junk food we all know and love that also fall in the realm of fats, carbohydrates and proteins (I'll digress on this further).

Carbohydrates

Carbs with a low GI provides longer energy

One of the primary fuel sources of our bodies is the breakdown product of most carbohydrates, which is glucose. Our bodies thrive from the energy generated via glycolysis, which is the chemical systematic process of breaking down glucose, transducing its stored energy into a chemical human energy currency known as ATP (an energy molecule that our bodies use to perform bodily functions). Glucose is so important that approximately 25 percent of the glucose we ingest is used for our brain functioning. This certainly accentuates how critical it is to maintain a normal blood sugar, so we can perform mental processes optimally and think clearly. Furthermore, it also brings to light the dilemma posed by diabetes as it pertains to insulin resistance or insulin absence, for insulin is the hormone that stimulates glucose to be taken up by our cells.

Failure for glucose to enter our cells prevents the generation of ATP by means of glycolysis, which translates to lower functional energy for our bodies. This is one of the reasons why avoiding carbs is a bad idea and why it is necessary to ingest the proper percentage (approximately 40 percent) so your body can do its job, helping you do yours. Understanding this on the biological level creates the platform for change, justifying its importance in your life—which brings us to the discussion of glycemic index.

Glycemic Index

Longer Energy GI 55 under   Shorter Energy GI 56–69r   Shortest Energy GI 70 higher

Glycemic index (or GI) is a numerical rating given to carbohydrates that distinguishes their food quality, so to speak. Foods with a low GI (55 and under), like fruits, vegetables, whole grains and nuts, take longer to digest and absorb, leading to steady induction in the blood stream, which helps to better regulate blood sugar and furthermore, energy levels. In other words, foods with a low GI minimize blood sugar spikes. Foods with a medium GI (56 to 69), like potatoes and whole-wheat products, break down more readily than low GI foods, while foods with a high GI (70 and above), such as white rice, breads and straight glucose, have more immediate release, causing blood sugar spikes that are unable to provide prolonged endurance.

Foods with a low GI minimize blood sugar spikes.

However, when we focus on eating low GI foods, we are eating for energy. Low GI foods have proven beneficial in reducing cholesterol and therefore, cardiovascular risk. They are better for helping us lose weight because of the sense of satiety they provide, thereby reducing hunger. They also help improve insulin sensitivity. Low GI foods help us feel more intact; together. Moreover, when it comes to energy, these foods help us to make it through the day without the sense of lulls. They help us for the long run. They help us endure what we've often fainted to endure. Low GI foods are what we must consistently *choose*; they're rarely foods of happenstance.

Proteins

Proteins help build up the body's muscle

Proteins are composed of amino acids. Proteins are important to our bodies because they are the basis by which our body's structure and mechanical processes are made, and they are essential in growth and repair. However, they are not our body's first (carbohydrates) or second (fats) line of energy generation. As mentioned previously, protein ingestion helps build up the body (anabolism), as in growth and muscle-building. People desiring to build muscle want to optimize their daily value of protein intake. Athletes and body builders know that more protein is the key to big gains. A general rule of thumb is 1g (gram) of protein per kg (kilogram) of body weight.

As important as protein intake is, it also is important to not go overboard with its ingestion. Excess of proteins can cause nephropathy or pathology of the kidneys, causing protein to be spilled over into the urine. All in all, proteins are a must if we are to grow our bodies strong and provide them proper nourishment. Proteins that I suggest are those such as the ones found in elite sources like salmon, nuts and soy/whey protein products. These types of foods are a richer source of nourishment and provide an alternative to red meat—though red meat obviously provides loads of protein and may be very tasty to some, it may not always be our best option. This is not to say don't eat red meat; I would say eat it in moderation.

Fats

Fats are nutritional, healing and provide energy

I think one of the most misconstrued macronutrients is fat, due to the word's conferred meaning to our psyche—that of it making us fat. However, fats are one of my favorite macronutrients to talk about because of their nutritional, healing and energy properties. Fats are essential for healthy skin and hair, nutrient integration and transport, temperature regulation and also (but not limited to) our body's defense. While it's true that overwhelming amounts of fat ingestion can lead to increased fat storage in the form of adipose tissue, this is more a concern when one exceeds the balanced diet proportion of 30 percent. While we all have adipose tissue (essential for insulation and energy storage), obese individuals (BMI greater than 30) have more.

Fats are one of my favorite macronutrients to talk about because of their nutritional, healing and energy properties.

Fat, our body's second-line energy producer, provides 9 Calories of energy per gram. When we talk about fat as a great source of macronutrients, the key is distinguishing between what I call *good fat* and *bad fat*. Good fat is fat from elite nutritious sources. These foods are usually high in monounsaturated and polyunsaturated fats (these descriptions refer to the type of chemical bond present in the carbon backbone chain of fats and how it relates to hydrogen).

Good Fat   Bad Fat

Foods such as almonds, fish oil, salmon and other cold-water fish, extra-virgin olive oil, olives, flaxseed and various seeds and nuts contain good fats. These types of fats have the potential to actually improve a person's cholesterol, along with fat's other benefits. Bad fats are those high in saturated and trans-fats. Trans-fats are the type you want to avoid at all costs, and actually nowadays, they are pretty hard to find because producers know they have more educated consumers who are more health-conscious. Saturated fats are found in a lot of processed foods, such as those that have a long shelf life. While it's often hard to avoid saturated fat in food products, my advice is to look at food nutritional labels and choose the product with the lower amount of saturated fat. (This is how I shop. We'll discuss this in a later chapter.)

Another benefit fats have that I would like to impress upon you is that fats protect us from disease. Fats can dilute potential pathogens, arresting them so they can either be excreted or destroyed by our immune system. This is just another wonderful benefit and reason why I like fats and want you to like them too. Fats are important. You need them; in fact, you cannot live without them. So now, when you think of fats, think of energy, health and protection rather than the unhealthy impression of getting fat.

Flying Over Grab and Go

Before I conclude this chapter on *fueling your engine with high-octane nutrition*, I want to digress on a topic I think undermines the importance of eating elite carbs, proteins and fats. So far, we've taken the time to discuss the significance of food energy and great macronutrients. However, I've found there is a place that interrupts such a rewarding conversation on a journey to more energy and elite health satisfaction. It's a place I often see people stop and catch a connecting flight to. Its destination is known as *The Land of Grab and Go.*

Here, there is always a layover. To get here you have to take a cheaper flight—a connecting flight. Direct flights are more expensive—of course. The point I want to bring out here is this: to connect here, you actually have to land here. You have to stop by. You have to get off the plane. Go to a new gate. Then wait. And a lot of times while you wait … you eat. You eat food you would not have eaten had you stayed in the air. You're laid over. The time to get to your final destination, *The Land of Satisfaction*, is delayed.

Why do we stop here when this is not our final destination?

I think we stop here because we think connecting here truly is *less expensive*. I think we think the alternative—the price of planning our own meals and preparing our food itinerary for the day, the week, the month— is too time-consuming, too over-the-top and simply just too much to do. So we take the cheaper flight to our final destination and in the process, add unwanted calories—unhealthy calories we did not plan. Over time, we get used to the cheaper flight—the connecting flight. We never think about flying directly or planning things out. We never think about upgrading to first class or having someone else plan out our meals. We settle with the connecting flight and the unplanned meals, thinking to ourselves, "This *is* my plan. I'll take the connecting, unplanned flight. I'll still get there. I'll still be satisfied."

Yet I submit to you that some of you will not; that is, be satisfied. This is the thing: It's funny, but the more often you take the connecting flight—that is, *grab and go*—you increase the chance for unexpected circumstances, happenstance or bad weather, so to speak. Your plans get delayed and delayed, until you're tired of having your health goals delayed. And you enter that cycle of not ever getting there, though your flight itinerary says you are supposed to get there.

The more often you take the connecting flight—that is, grab and go— you increase the chance for unexpected circumstances, happenstance or bad weather, so to speak.

You know what I mean: You can go to work throughout the week and on a particular day instead of packing your own lunch, you stop at FatBoy Subs—albeit unplanned—because you chose to not think things through the night before. You think to yourself, "This is just one day. It's no big deal. My health will survive—it'll manage. What's one day?" But then it happens again. You take the cheaper flight. You eat out again without concern for how it affects your blood pressure, your cholesterol, your weight—your energy. You don't even think about your health. You subconsciously don't care, though you consciously do ... but not at the moment.

And all of a sudden you get into a flow ... but it's a backward rhythm. A WellSpring in reverse. You habitually take the cheaper flight and eating out throughout the week is just the thing you do. And here's the kicker: You then come in to see me in the clinic and ask me why you can never drop the weight, lower your cholesterol, improve your blood pressure or have more energy. You think there must be a pill, a diet, a plan. And unfortunately there's not. You took the cheaper flight.

Friend, think higher. Pay the price of planning out your food itinerary. Take the direct flight. It's more expensive, but it'll cost you less in the long run. And that's what we want: the long run. We want to live longer—live better. And in order to do this we have to plan things out. We have to take the direct flight. I submit to you that we must consciously plan our food itinerary forward throughout the week, so that we control what we ingest and only eat meals with the intent to provide us better health and more energy. If we do this we can also plan to eat the foods we love—you know, the ones we mostly eat unplanned: the cookies, pies, cakes, etc.

We must consciously plan our food itinerary forward throughout the week, so that we control what we ingest and only eat meals with the intent to provide us better health and more energy.

Don't get me wrong—I am not saying eating for health means eating foods we don't like. Instead, I'm saying eating for health means we are eating foods higher in caloric quality and with lower glycemic index. Usually what happens is the cookies, pies, cakes, etc., that we *grab and go* with are without regard to caloric quality and glycemic index, and so we eat unregulated and without a sense of navigation or gauge as to how these foods are affecting our energy levels throughout the day. But if we plan a time or day where we are going to eat more vicariously, we can control our health travel and yet feel as if we are flying wherever the wind takes us. This is how we can eat what we want and still arrive on time, escaping the legalism of only eating foods we think taste like grass all week (I'm only humoring you).

But seriously: Plan to eat, and eat well. If you'll take the time and pay the higher price—the direct flight—you'll fly over The Land of Grab and Go, costing yourself less in the long run. You'll eat for higher energy and better health. You won't tire as easily or feel sick as much. You'll be able to regulate your strength, feeling better about yourself. And if you'll do this, you'll be able *to do*—your life, with your engine being fueled and fully energized with high-octane nutrition.

Chapter Ten

I remember one day in my clinic I was talking to one of the farmers I would routinely take care of. Large man. Burly. Strong hands. 55. Overweight. His cholesterol numbers were off, I mean sky high! I asked him if he was exercising and just as soon as I asked that I thought to myself, "Uh-oh … here it comes." This gentleman looked at me as if to say, "Boy, I get up at 3 o'clock—when I hit the farm house… ." Well … that's kind of what he said. He explained to me, "I get up at three. I'm milking cows by five. I'm moving haystacks. Plowing fields …" Get the point? After he was finished, I paused to take into account what he had said. I then fired back a question as I began my counterargument.

I asked him, "How long have you been working like that?" He replied, "Since I was fourteen." He fell into my trap. Now it was time to drive my point home. "So if you were working out since you were fourteen, you pretty much have been doing this your whole entire life—which means that, in essence, you have plateaued." I further said to him, "You see, to me what you do is exercise but to you it's no longer exercise—because you're used to it. It's no longer a challenge." I continued to tell him, "I could not do what you do, nor could the average person. But what you do no longer is effective for you."

I love this story. I use it all the time because it paints the picture for this chapter. E^2 stands for *effective exercise*. It's exercise that changes your numbers. It changes the numbers for your blood pressure, cholesterol and weight. Bottom line: E^2 makes you more effective. Its outcome equals more energy for you.

So-Called Exercising at Work

Let me digress. I cannot begin to tell you the number of times I will ask a patient if they are exercising and I receive the response, "Oh, I'm very busy at work," or "I'm always working or lifting on my job."

That's nice. But again, if your blood pressure, cholesterol and weight are not changing, your exercising at work is not working. Don't get me wrong. Listen to my heart on this. I'm not saying that because you are not challenging yourself that this is the only reason your numbers are not right. I am saying that because you are not challenging yourself, your numbers are not right. Meaning it's not the *only* reason, but it is a reason. You see, you have to do all you can do to live healthier. Sometimes walking from the desk to the copy machine 10 times won't do it. And I want you to see that. I love telling the man or woman who tells me in the clinic that while they're doing X-Y-Z at work, they're doing A-B-C to exercise. I say, "Really?"— because that type of explanation doesn't work well for me when I talk to my wife.

You see, you have to do all you can do to live healthier.

If I am talking to my wife, Rheami, while I'm texting with my iPhone over dinner on a night out, I find that she doesn't seem to like that too much. But I'm like, "I'm talking and texting … I'm doing both." OK—let me digress here again. Gentlemen, if you're talking to your wife, do nothing else. Focus on her. Look. Listen. Nothing else.

Back to my point. Rheami (women in general) does not see "talking and texting" as talking. Likewise, exercising, water cooler trips and making copies don't mix either. I mean, if it's truly effective, go for it. But I can provide countless numbers—in my experience from the vitals and labs of men and women in my clinic—that say the opposite.

The point being: You need an isolated, set-apart time to exercise. When you do this, you are focused on being effective at accomplishing your health goals and nothing else. You have to get down to the nitty-gritty when it comes to making lifestyle modifications. Lifestyle modification is all about habitual change and not just a mere result. Instead, it's about results because you're constantly improving, working, going, pushing. It's a habit. But habits start small.

The Littleton Principle

When I am starting out a patient on a regimen of exercise, I start small. Remember the Littleton Principle: *Little* changes make a *Ton* of difference. And they do. I always tell the patient, "I want you to give me five minutes of exercise three times a week" (of course this is after I break them through the barrier of thinking exercise at work counts). That's 15 minutes in a week. I make it simple. The patient often responds, "I can do more than that! I'll give you thirty."

Remember the Littleton Principle: **Little** *changes make a* **Ton** *of difference.*

Let me digress … just between me and you, there's no way on God's green earth they are going to give me 30. If they were going to give me 30, they would not need any of the exercise advice that I had already begun telling them.

Recently I was reading a book by Robert Kiyosaki called *Unfair Advantage*. It's a book about financial education in our new economy. In his book, Kiyosaki talks about the difference between capital gains and cash flow. *Capital gains* simply means you cash in on an investment that you bought low and sold high. You made the difference. *Cash flow* is not the financial difference from something you sold when its value increased. Instead, cash flow is the new stream of income that continually yields increase into your pocket—a true asset. Kiyosaki believes in financial education—I do too, and I also believe in energy education (another E^2). In energy education, my goal is to introduce into your life streams of health.

"I'll give you thirty." That's a capital gain. I am not interested in how much they can give me. I'm interested in whether they are going to work out tomorrow. And the next day. And so on and so forth. I'm interested in helping them form a habit leading to streams of health. I'm interested in habitual change. I tell people all the time, "You have to make exercise like brushing your teeth; in some form or matter, you have to do it every day." Experts say it takes 21 days to form a habit; I (also an expert!) say focus on what you're doing until you don't have to focus on what you're doing. When you do this, you've formed a habit; however long it takes you. Now, if my patient will work out three times a week for five minutes, when this routine becomes established, I'll increase him up to 10, 15, 20, 25 and eventually 30 minutes three times a week. But you have to start somewhere and starting small always counts, because it's something you can have confidence in to reproduce!

Your Target Heart Rate

Here's another story: I have a couple of patients who do everything. They walk. They golf. They dance. They golf. My point is they golf. They golf about three times a week. (I'm envious.) So when I ask them, "How's your exercise coming?" "Doc, I'm always golfing—at least three times a week." Really?

Let me digress … golf … oh golf. Honestly, God bless golf.

But if golf, like the iconic exercise people always tell me they do—*walking*—ain't cutting numbers … it's not effective.

The key here is to get your heart rate up and quicken your respiratory rate. I tell people all the time that if you are not increasing your heart and respiratory rate, I don't care if you are playing 10 rounds of golf or walking 10 miles—it's not cutting it. Unless you're 85, have arthritis and walk with a 4-wheeled walker, then maybe walking is cutting it. For the 85-year-old in this example, walking is great. All I want from this 85-year-old is to *move* and we'll increase from there.

The key here is to get your heart rate up and quicken your respiratory rate.

So how high do you have to get your heart rate up when you're exercising? Good question—the right question.

When you exercise you want to perform "moderate to vigorous" intensity activity. A way to measure this is by knowing your target heart rate. You want to shoot for at least 50 percent of your maximum heart rate. A simple way to approximate this is to subtract your age from 220. Multiply the difference by 50 percent (for the low target range), and then multiply the difference by 85 percent (for the high target range). This calculation now gives you your average age-adjusted target heart rate range when exercising.

So for example, if we take our 55-year-old farmer and subtract 220 from 55, we get 165. Now we multiply 165 by 0.5 (50 percent), which equals 82.5 or 83 bpm (beats per minute). Furthermore, we take 165 again and multiply it by 0.85 (85 percent), which equals 140.25 or 140 bpm. So our 55-year-old, large, burly, overweight farmer must increase his heart rate within 83 to 140 bpm to be effective while milking cows! Not happening. So instead I recommend he go for a walk—a power walk.

The Perfect Exercise

Once in a while people ask me what is the number one exercise I recommend when it comes to working out. First, I tell them if they want to improve their numbers, lifting dumbbells won't do (well, not completely). Instead, I redirect them. Instead of anaerobic exercise (lifting weights), I direct them to aerobic exercise (cardiovascular exercise, or in other words, things that get your heart rate up). Being originally from Michigan (where it snows) people told me all the time, "Doc, I can't run because there's a foot of snow on the ground."

Let me digress … Somebody should have told that to Rocky in *Rocky IV* when he was fighting the Russian Ivan Drago in Russia during Christmas. Uh, I think there was snow on the ground … yeah, I believe there was.

Anyway, I responded to those patients, "OK—then ride a bike." A bike? Yes, a stationary one. My number one exercise for you to get started with is to ride a stationary bike inside for five minutes three times a week. It's an excuse eliminator! You can watch TV, ride—even text on the phone (that's for you Rheami)—I don't care. But you are riding and there's no snow excuse. We eliminated the snow day. You have to go in to work out. Another reason I love the stationary bike is because it protects your back, because you are seated. Your knees are relieved that they are not carrying all your weight. It's doable so you can do it again tomorrow. And that's what we want—to form a habit by doing it again, tomorrow.

My number one exercise for you to get started with is to ride a stationary bike inside for five minutes three times a week.

Give Me What You Got

One more brief story: The other day I had a patient who was very obese. He was so obese he could only partially walk. In fact, that's what he said when I asked him about exercise. "OK," I said, "then partially walk for five minutes." I told him that you have to give me what you got. We'll go from there.

You see, there's no excuse to giving what you have. We all have something. Exercise is important—it's vital. And as a doctor, I care so much for everyone who walks through my clinic doors and everyone I connect with (which means you) and that you do what you must to unleash your talents, gifts, personality— U to the world—so that I can benefit. But not just me—I want your family, loved ones and society to benefit from the gifts you have. I want to lengthen your days. I want you to live your full time on this earth so you can do your purpose here. Exercise is vital to carry this through, because if you'll exercise, you'll improve your blood pressure, lower your cholesterol and lose weight—thereby, having more energy *to do* your life.

Chapter Eleven

There are some basic things that you should know. And if you know them—and do them—you can have elite health. Elite health is your best health and more. It's health that others marvel at—even envy. It is the health that, well … if you'll be honest with me … you secretly wished you always had. The only thing is that you have to believe it is for you—that it's attainable. Once you accept this, then you'll understand the laws that govern elite health. After that, all that is left to do is execute the principles.

Here in this chapter, I want to cause you to see that elite health is for you. I want to teach you the four laws that govern it. And I want to teach you how to practice these laws to have it.

Elite Health is for U

In our journey, we are now preparing to land. And as we descend, preparing to touch down in our new place, we must think larger. Leaving things behind and entering into a better place means we have to see things differently. We must think higher. Otherwise, we'll make this a round-trip ticket and go back. But do not go back. We're almost here. We're almost at our destination.

As we begin to come into *The Land of Satisfaction*, it's fine time to be satisfied with your personal health. The vision you see in your mind's eye of being trimmer, toner and more energized is the elite you. That far-off notion you sometimes have about how nice it would be if you did not have to catch your usual cold or that seasonal flu that they say is the new H1N1 epidemic—yeah, that's a vision of the elite you, too.

This new place of being your best and having energy to do your best is all about elitism. I want you to think this way because like I discussed with you in my first chapter, U, *you* have unique talents, abilities and a purpose that is special and unique that others need—that I need.

Let me take an aside for a second and say this. I feel (I literally feel) that as I write on health elitism, some of you do not like that I speak of such things. You may have a difficult time receiving this because you do not like the notion of a position of being better or higher than something else. I know that some of you do not like the fact that in this book I talk about arriving and accepting that you have arrived. Well, I'll just say this: If you do not strive to be your best or elite, you're still striving for something. Some of you are striving to be average. And if you are not striving at all, by default you indirectly strive to be worse.

Friend, listen, you do not have to be elite in what *I do* but I urge you to be elite in what *you do*. Just do you. You—*unleashed*—are elite. And you have to think this way; otherwise you will not put any gravity to becoming better and improving if you only think that the end result will still be average and not remarkable or elite. And in order to be truly exceptional in what you do, you have to have elite health so you can do your life on the platform of corporeal well-being.

You—unleashed—are elite.

I tell my patients all the time that I want them to be healthy so they can live all their days on this earth *to do* their life. You don't want to have to visit the doctor three days a week or miss work or miss engagements. Missing things leads to regret. I remember when I was in the 8th grade, I was a part of an elite group of students who flew to Paris, France, for a 13-day exchange student study abroad. In order to qualify for such a trip I had to take an oral test in front of the high school instructors, whereby I had to undergo an interview for the trip. The test was that the interview was in *French*. Long story short, I qualified and went to Paris. What a beautiful trip! Literally, it was awesome! Except for one little thing. And this little thing has stayed with me to this day.

Out of all the sightseeing I did and the pictures I took, the one thing I failed to see was the Louvre—the museum where the Mona Lisa is kept. This may not seem like a big deal to you but to me it's big … and I regret it. It turns out that on the day the group of students I was with went to the Louvre, I was sick with a headache and stayed in my room in bed. I have not been back to Paris since. Sure, I've seen the Mona Lisa several times. Who hasn't? But I've never seen the real one. I've never taken in that moment or appreciated what it felt like to be there. I cannot tell you how deep the colors Leonardo Da Vinci used on the Mona Lisa really are. I have no stories about this moment—*at least not yet.*

Read the heart of what I'm saying: I'm not saying expect never again to have a headache cause you to miss an important moment in your life, but what I am leading up to saying is that if I can prepare myself to live at my healthy best, then I can prevent a lot of random sicknesses and occurrences. Now if you're thinking, *Jason … come on … be realistic; you can't stop headaches*, then friend I say to you, "I am (being realistic)"—think higher!

Now I know I was just in 8ᵗʰ grade at the time and I didn't know what I know now. To be honest, I was not even thinking about elite health at the time. But had I known; had my life been shaped that way, oh the difference it might have made. But now that I am telling you, you can tell your 8ᵗʰ grader or help improve the life of your 2ⁿᵈ grader. Bottom line: Believe you can have your best health.

The 4 Elite Health Laws

In general, there are four laws that govern elite health. And these laws are so common that their end result—elite health—is so uncommon; this is because people time and again either think they are doing them or simply underestimate them. I see it all the time.

When patients come in to see me for a common cold, I tell them they have a common cold—a virus. They tell me, "Give me an antibiotic." I tell them, "Antibiotics won't work for this." They don't believe me because what they are feeling and experiencing is greater than fact. There is no cure (as of right now) for the viral common cold. Antibiotics irradiate bacteria, not viruses. The number one rule of medicine is *do no harm*. Number two is *the patient knows his/her body better than me*. OK … let me be honest, there is no number two rule (I just made that up) but all the same it's still true.

Anyway, what ends up happening is that sometimes I stick to my guns and do not prescribe an antibiotic and sometimes I don't stick to my guns and I actually prescribe an antibiotic. And the patient gets better, not because of the chemistry with the antibiotic but because their body was going to overcome the illness regardless. All I do is remember rule number three: *treat the patient, not the illness*. So sometimes I write the prescription because I forsake not rule number four, *the placebo effect*, meaning if my patient thinks it's helping—it's helping. (Colleagues, those of you who are staunch about this—please!—don't write me any letters or send any hate mail … I'm somewhat kidding … somewhat.)

Either way, *to write or to not write an antibiotic*, that's not the question. The question is, what are you going to do to support your body when you are under the weather? That's the question. Because the answer to this is the platform for elite health and this is where the four Elite Health Laws (not the four rules of medicine) come in. I tell my patients in conjunction with their prescription (if I write one) that they have to execute these four things to help their body overcome this ailment effectively and quickly. So here we go.

The question is, what are you going to do to support your body when you are under the weather?

Law Number One: *Move!*

I know … intuitive, right? Well, let's find out. I know we discussed physical activity in Chapter Ten, but we'll discuss it further here because there are some things you should know in general about it. Intuitively, we know exercise can make you healthier (to a degree), and also, exercise can make you healed! Listen, when you are feeling under the weather, the last thing you want to do is exercise. Instead, you want to get some chicken soup and lay out on the couch—and I'm not condemning this. But you also want to exercise. Our bodies are made with a lymphatic system, whereby healing white blood cells and other immune products travel through, as they do in the blood.

The only difference is that unlike the blood, the fluid traveling within your lymphatic system does not directly have a heart to drive the flow, like your cardiovascular system. Instead, our lymphatic system flow is driven in a lot of ways by our movement. A watered-down way of saying it is it flows when we move. And one of the main activities that gets us really moving is when we exercise. I always take aback patients feeling under the weather when I tell them this first law—the law of exercise. It's an eye opener for them a lot of times. But I tell them if they'll exercise just a little bit, they'll start to feel better faster, not only because of the flow of healing products, but also, the release of the body feel-good chemicals we often talk about, such as endorphins.

Exercise and increased activity are keys to having elite health. You have to stay fit. You were not meant to live a sedentary life. Exercise helps to promote a healthy heart and cardiovascular system. It also helps to prevent stiffness from inactivity—this is especially important in the case of rheumatoid arthritis and some other arthritic morbidity. But here's the key: like anything else for the most part, you do not want to overdo exercise. You want to exercise to stay fit.

If you play professionally or compete athletically, you want to exercise and train to be at the top of your game. However, you do not want to overdo it. When we train, especially strength train, we break down muscle in order to build it again. Muscle turnover occurs anyway. However, when we overdo physical activity, the body does not see this as routine turnover; instead, it sees training as injury and responds accordingly through immunological pathways. I submit to you that over-training is counterproductive. Long-term, the body perceives this as being hurt time and again. Over-training is a life-waster and may shorten your life; likewise, your energy.

But here's the key: like anything else for the most part, you do not want to overdo exercise. You want to exercise to stay fit.

How many high-impact athletes do you know that live well into their 80s and 90s? I recently found an article discussing how the diets of athletes may be harmful due to the fact that their diets are usually high in calories, increasing the chance for larger amounts of destructive free radicals to interact with their bodies. Also, the wear and tear they endure, if you think about it, is not good. Look at football, for example: players line up to fall down time and again. This is just not good for the joints and connective tissue, not including the continual mass building that must take place in order to compete at that level, a lot of times buttressed even more by commercialized supply and demand and the need to train harder in order to make the cut, get a higher signing bonus, or fill more seats. Not good.

Taking everything in balance, train moderately. Stay fit, achieve your natural BMI, and improve your numbers. Train to live a fruitful, long life. Other than the stationary bike and bike riding (which I recommended as the #1 exercise for my patients), I also recommend swimming. I love to swim. This is my plan to stay in shape long-term. In addition, if you want to lose weight fast, swimming is one of the best ways to do it. Swimming burns calories like nobody's business. This is why when you are finished swimming, you feel this intense hunger once you get out of the pool. You feel like you can eat a horse—literally. With swimming, you are moving more muscles comparatively and continuously than any other sport. You are toning anaerobically (as in muscle training) as well as profiting aerobically (as in increasing your cardiovascular benefit). Also, with swimming, you are padding your joints because of hydraulic buoyancy.

I had a patient recently who sprained her ankle. She had just started a workout program at my advice, to lose weight and achieve her natural BMI. The ankle sprain was seen as a setback, but to me, I saw it as an opportunity to launch off into another form of exercise. I told my patient to try exercising in the pool to not only rehabilitate her ankle, but also to continue burning calories. From my previous discussions with this patient, she already understood that the rule of thumb is to work on losing 500 food calories (in terms of the average 2,000 food calorie diet) a day—3,500 calories a week—in order to lose one pound of mass toward her goals. She tried it, and continued her quest toward her natural BMI and staying fit. Listen, you just can't beat swimming. I've seen overweight professional baseball players but I've never seen overweight Olympic swimmers. I just think it's simply the best sport to do.

Before I go on, I want to leave you with this: With all exercise, it is important to stretch. I recommend stretching after you exercise. Before you start your activity, warm up by doing some light movement to get the muscles moving and to accelerate your heart rate. A light jog or even jumping jacks or other calisthenics will serve to prime your body for the more intense activity to come. Calisthenics are a form of dynamic exercise, which prepares your body by lengthening and stretching the muscles you're preparing to use more dynamically in your endeavored activity. After you're done with your workout, stretch. This is a great way to cool down and prevent resulting injury. I encourage you to stretch on your off days. This way, you stay long, strong and limber throughout your week. Also, stretching helps you feel healthier. It also keeps the healing white blood cells moving round and round. If you'll stretch and stay active, soon you'll develop the habit of routinely doing so. And eventually, you won't feel right if you miss a day or slack off. So stay active!

Law Number Two: *Eat!*

Intuitive, right? Maybe for some! But there are a lot of you who don't eat much at all. And when you do eat, you eat the wrong stuff! A lot of you wake up 35 minutes before work and quickly shower, throw on clothes and rush out the door. Some of you actually take a second to stop by the refrigerator (which you should—to EAT!) only to grab an energy drink, thinking this is all you need for some quick calories or that's all you have time for, or even worse, hoping for a quick boost—an eye opener, per se. The problem is, you give your body nothing to work with to fuel its engine to take you the long haul for the day. Moreover, you've given your body nothing to work with (as far as nutritional needs) to help support your body's immune system to fight off … um … let's say … a viral cold? Eating nutritional meals is vital to having elite health. Furthermore, eating breakfast is vital to having elite health.

Eating breakfast is analogous to fueling up a plane in preparation for takeoff. I don't know about you, but I'm not getting on any plane 1/8 past empty, talking about "seats upright, cell phones off, we're preparing to take off." You must eat breakfast. And when you do, eat light. Eating three stacks of pancakes with butter and syrup along with sausage, eggs and hash browns sounds good, but the reality is, that puts you to sleep instead of providing energy. Bottom line—it weighs you down. Pilots know if their aircraft is carrying too much weight, not even the law of aerodynamics will get them off the ground like they want to.

Instead, I recommend a breakfast of fruit, yogurt and perhaps oatmeal to start the day. For some power punch, include a protein shake or mix some whey or soy in your oatmeal. To top things off, consider ingesting some flaxseed oil and elite fat! This is one of renowned physical trainer and health expert Chris Johnson's recommendations to improving overall mental acuity and body dynamics, and I agree. Flaxseed oil is the oil for your engine to take you over the top. Remember, elite fats contain nine calories per gram (more than carbs and proteins), and these elite calories can be readily used for high-impact energy. You can take a tablespoon of flaxseed oil with your breakfast or put it on your oatmeal, or even mix it in your protein shake. Either way, consider it.

So disregard your opinion or practice of not eating breakfast; for chemically, the basis for Law #2 is that energy *in* allows for effective work *out*—and by *out*, I mean, effective work out of *you*. You need energy to do work; any physicist knows this! But I tell people all the time, especially when they are under the weather, that one of the things you need to do is eat your way to health—but eat elite macronutrients like I talked about in Chapter Ten (I will further break down examples of elite foods to eat in my upcoming book called *The WellSpring Diet*).

I recommend, in general, that you have six meals a day. Eat breakfast, lunch and dinner with a snack in between breakfast and lunch, lunch and dinner, and dinner and bedtime. This way, you keep your blood sugar on an even keel, allowing for a steady release of nutrient energy into your day. My favorite snacks are almonds and blueberries. If you want elite energy and if you want to function optimally, consider this in between meals. Blueberries are some of the best carbs around and they also provide an excellent combo of elite fat and protein to fuel you optimally. Of course there are other food options; in general, try to always make your snack both a fruit/vegetable and a whole grain. You can always mix some soy yogurt/dairy in the mix. It's up to you.

But understand that whatever you do, developing a consistent routine of eating fruits and vegetables in your daily snacks employs the daily and necessary antioxidants you need to fight off destructive free radicals that age you, and also lead to destructive medical conditions like cancers and other chronic illnesses. The bottom line is, do your research. I want you to eat for purpose and productivity. Find out what foods you like and determine if they are worthy enough to be eating—like in the case of carbs, eat only carbs with a low glycemic index (further discussed in *The WellSpring Diet*). For those who pray over their meal like I do, a quick and dirty way to tell if something's good for you or not is whether you feel funny praying over it! Sometimes it doesn't feel right when I pray over a whole bunch of chocolate cake, but it sure tastes good!

I want you to eat for purpose and productivity.

In addition to this, when you eat, eat organic! Organic products, though more expensive, are in general healthier across the board. Your health is invaluable. Spend the money to eat foods free of extra additives and pesticides. This is one of the main reasons why people become sick and have low energy. It's not that eating non-organic products will kill you; it's just that, over time, some of the extra unnecessary chemicals ingested allow for cancer and illness to develop, and it's these things that will kill you. If going totally organic is too much, then go organic with foods with thin skin—like apples, grapes and plums. Things like oranges, bananas and pineapples are layered with a thicker coverage, further protecting the fruit from harmful chemicals. Whatever you do, go organic. Organic is a *life extender* and I believe the more your diet is composed of it, the better and longer you can live with a higher quality of energy—a more elite type.

Here, I'd like to also take a second to talk about vitamins. Eating essential vitamins and nutrients are important. For the most part, we can obtain an excellent variety of essential vitamins and nutrients from the foods we eat—especially organic. But I'm also aware that a lot of our foods are so processed and non-organic that they do not have the same quality of essential vitamins and nutrients that foods used to have before nutrition became so commercialized. That's why vitamins are so important to intake. I recommend that you take a multivitamin every day to provide additional antioxidants and other benefits to fight destructive processes that can occur in the body.

People always ask me what vitamins they should partake. I tell them, usually, to make sure to get a lot of vitamin C, which is essential in healing and wound repair. I'm also big on vitamin D. Vitamin D, as of recent, has been thought to not only be important in bone health but to also be essential in energy health as well. Vitamin D is mostly obtained from the sun's interaction with our skin. The more sun we receive, usually the higher our vitamin D levels. When I practiced medicine in Michigan, most of my patients—of all races—were deficient in this essential energy producer. This was because of the latitude we were at and the degree of sun we received there. However, when I moved to Florida and started practicing here, it was mostly my patients with darker complexions that were low in vitamin D, and this was mostly because while darker skin may add some benefit against the harmful effects of the sun, it also limits the amount of vitamin D that can be produced.

Everyone is different and everyone has a specific food Rx. I have patients who can only eat certain things. They cannot have strawberries, for example, but they can have blueberries. Or they cannot have cow-based products, but they can have soy. Find out what resonates with your body and eat the elite. People do have food conditions such as Inflammatory Bowel Disease (IBD), Irritable Bowel Syndrome (IBS), Celiac disease and other digestive conditions that do not permit for certain foods to be eaten—understandable. So find your specific food Rx and optimize it through creative meal planning.

Find out what resonates with your body and eat the elite.

Law Number Three: *Drink!*

Intuitive, right? But let's just see. If you're going to drink, drink something healthy—like water. Intuitive, right? Not so. Water is the physical makeup of all living things. We need water to live. It can be said this way: we are 60 percent water. The functioning of all our cells and all the chemical reactions that take place in our body depend on this very essential solvent. However, I find all too often that we squander this remarkable necessity in our body by either not drinking enough or drinking things that cause us to lose the water we have, such as alcohol and caffeinated drinks, which act as diuretics to our bodies. In Chris Johnson's book *Meal Patterning*, he talks about how 75 percent of Americans are chronically dehydrated, contributing to illnesses such as renal disease, bronchitis, asthma, skin problems and other maladies like headaches (if only I had drunk more water when I was in 8th grade …). Seventy-five percent! That's a lot. This means to me that most people do not know they are dehydrated! Very sad.

OK … you're dehydrated … well, likely you are, according to the statistic. Drink water—but be strategic. I recommend that you drink water in between meals. Drink organic juices with your meals, for the health benefit. In general, drinking juice with your meals works as a better solvent to help your digestive system process and absorb your meal better. This is because your body sees the juice chemically as a food and processes the juice—and the meal—all the same, whereas water can lengthen the digestive process or cause food material to be absorbed improperly. So instead, consider staggering your water intake. Drink an 8-ounce glass of water first thing in the morning, then an 8-ounce glass between breakfast and lunch (let's say 10 a.m.). And finally, drink another 8-ounce glass around 2 p.m. between lunch and dinner.

Drink water—but be strategic.

"That's only twenty-four ounces of pure water," you might say. What about 64 ounces of water a day (or eight 8-ounce glasses)? The answer is simple. Because all liquids contain water one way or another, the juice you drink during your meals and snacks will make up the other 40 ounces. You do not have to drink eight 8-ounce glasses of water a day. Because you think that you actually will never accomplish that goal because it can be consistently overwhelming, asking you to drink 24 ounces of water instead of 64 ounces is doable and easy. The key is to stay away from diuretic-like fluids such as caffeine and alcohol, so as not to be a part of the statistic.

Finally, let's talk about the energy drink. Our society is inundated with the latest and greatest energy tonics. This goes to show you how powerful marketing can be. The energy drinks these days now come with a promise of how long you'll feel energized. But don't buy them just for that. These drinks, while providing you with increased alertness and another few hours in overtime, are not the root answer to providing you more energy *to do* your life. It's foolishness to sum up the art of doing your life to the kick of energy you get from drinking these commercialized drinks. When you do this, you are saying, "My energy *to do* my life depends on a caffeinated drink." Don't do this! It's sucking out the water in you and there's something about water and you that's so important energy-wise.

Hey, I drink an energy drink now and then, like when I am on call at the hospital or if I am driving late—but this is not routine. My energy *to do* life is not dependent on this. But some of yours is. And you know it. That's why you're here with me, reading this book. You know you've become an energy drink junkie, or even worse, you've become an energy drink chemist, able to tell others the best blend on energy drinks to intake *to do* your day. As an energy chemist, you can tell me which drink gives you a longer kick, because you sampled them all as you became more aware of your increasing tolerance to them, trying more caffeinated alternatives. Soon, all that happens is you feel overall run-down, sluggish and flat-out tired. You feel unhealthy and fat. You start thinking to yourself, *Maybe I ought to see a doctor because I just don't feel healthy.* Listen friend, energy drinks were never meant to support your health—your healthy habits were.

OK, I hear some of you saying, "Dr. Jason ... what about coffee? I can't do without my coffee." *Fine, drink coffee.* But understand you're losing water. Think about how many times you run to the bathroom afterward. So do this: Either drink decaffeinated (yeah right!) or add another 8-ounce glass of water for every coffee cup you intake. Balance it out. There is nothing wrong with coffee; I kind of like it. But my drink is lemonade. Did you know that lemonade also serves another health purpose, other than making me happier because of the taste?

Lemonade can prevent certain types of kidney stones from forming because of the chemistry behind it. The most common type of kidney stone is the calcium oxalate stone. Lemonade contains citric acid. The quid pro quo of it is, the citric acid in lemonade will substitute with oxalate, forming calcium citrate (a non-stone formulation) instead of calcium oxalate stones. And as a side note … another one of my favorite drinks is hot chocolate. Hot chocolate can serve as a source of antioxidants, and also the temperature of the hot chocolate is known to relieve symptoms of mucus drainage and other cold disturbances (just like any warm fluid would do). This is *health2consider*.

On the subject of the other diuretic-like fluid, alcohol, the *general medical view* would say to limit consumption. However, *my view* is, don't drink it at all. Alcohol is not a life-extender; it's a life-waster. It serves no functional benefit for you. OK, I hear some of you saying, "Dr. Jason, drinking alcohol in moderation helps with heart disease." OK … but so do a lot of other healthy things. Hey, marijuana helps with glaucoma! But I'm not advocating it. Get the picture?

I had a patient in the clinic the other day tell me they only socially drink, when I asked them during the course of a history and physical whether they drink alcohol. (When you ask a person if they drink, ask them *how much* they drink, otherwise you'll always get a minimalist answer. One time I asked someone if they consumed alcohol and they said yes, only one drink a day. It wasn't until I asked how much that I learned it was a 40-ounce!) Anyway, back to my patient. He said he only would have four to five drinks per occasion, and this was once a month. I told him that binge drinking was not good and that I had concerns for his liver function.

I told him what the *general medical view* was, but instead, he asked me what *my view* was. Since he asked—and I'm glad he did—I told him to consider not drinking at all. This took him aback. And he was astonished by the fact that I do not drink. I simply told him that it is a personal choice and that I am focused on living all my days out in my best health—my elite health—so that I can do the life I enjoy. Long story short, when I saw him in follow-up, he was so moved by my personal story that he stopped drinking altogether. I am not telling you what to do. There's the general medical view and then there's my view. Make *your own* decision. But the bottom line is—drink water.

Law Number Four: *Sleep!*

Intuitive, right? Not so fast! One of the top five patient complaints I get is insomnia. It makes sense that if you can't sleep, it's hard to have energy. Sleeping is so important (lazy people, please disregard my emphasis here) to your health and energy. Sleeping recharges you. It's rest for the body. In Section Two of this book, we talked about mental rest or rest for the mind, which is important, but if you do not rest your body, even if feeling mentally recharged, there's a limit to what your body will perform. You have to obtain adequate sleep. Now for different people this means different things. The *general medical view* is that you need seven to nine hours of sleep per night. And I agree with this. In fact, I need eight hours to feel tip-top. However, this is not always realistic.

Being a physician, I know this all too well. With my sometimes unpredictable schedule, especially when on call, finding time to sleep can be a challenge. Besides that, I'm always driven to do more—always trying to accomplish something else. And because of this, sometimes I'm operating on maybe five to six hours of rest, sometimes much less. With this said, the bottom line is, I still have to do what I have to do—see patients and accomplish goals. There's no end. But my perspective is that I am here on earth *to do* life—mine, and I feel like I have so much *to do*. The reality is that we all have much *to do*. The problem is most of us don't know what our *to dos* really are. And this is why I say all the time to patients who find themselves in this place that you literally have to sit down, get a pen and a pad, and write out your dreams. Get to know yourself (Remember Julia Roberts' character in *Runaway Bride*—Chapter One?). It starts here.

So what does all this about *to dos* have "to do" with sleep? Much! Sleep has its own function—again, to recharge you. You're being recharged to be charged. Charged for what? Life! You have to take the perspective that you are sleeping to get up again—not to stay down! Don't get me wrong, sleeping is pleasurable. When I sleep, I take pleasure in it. I also am out like a light switch and can wake up at the drop of a pin. But I sleep long and deep and it is always restful and peaceful.

I'm going to share with you how I do it so that you can consider my strategies, and hopefully, incorporate them for yourself. But before I discuss my sleep regimen, I want to make sure you understand my point about having the right perspective about sleep. The bottom line is this: You want to take the perspective that *I am sleeping to refresh myself so I can get up again to live. I don't want to sleep more than I need to and when possible I don't want to necessarily sleep less than required. And when I sleep, I plan to enjoy it.* That last part, "I plan to enjoy it," should also be your expectation.

Friend, listen—I have counseled more people than you know on how to obtain great sleep. It's a common worldwide problem. And the people you would not think have sleep problems do. One of the common things I see is tolerance to sleep medication. For some, great sleep has become synonymous with the latest and greatest insomnia medication. Some of these medications can be very addicting and bad for your long-term health. I cannot begin to tell you the countless number of times people in my clinic have sworn by their inability to sleep unless they have their medication. A lot of times, some of my patients with sleep disorders do not care about changing their sleep habits to obtain better sleep in the long run, but instead, they care about only getting to sleep *tonight*. And so they want their meds. And I cannot begin to tell you what people will do and say if they do not get their medication. Sometimes, it's awful. And you know what I see in all this? I see a person whose energy, sleep and even life is at the mercy of a pill. My heart goes out to them, and this is one of the reasons why I stand on my soapbox to help them and you obtain remarkable sleep.

When we talk about obtaining great sleep, we talk about practicing a bedtime routine, which—in order for it to work—must become habit. Even if you are taking sleep medication, it is important for you not to just lie down and do nothing, allowing the pill to do all the work. You have to practice certain effective, time-tested habits regardless. But here's what I hear all the time: "I tried it and it didn't work." My heart, once again, goes out to people who take on this perspective about effective principles, only being committed to something they know deep down is worthwhile, only to quit at a point. When it comes to effective principles, you have to work them until they work in you. Period. If I were taking a sleep aid, I'm going to take the sleep aid and work on proper sleep habits until I no longer need the sleep aid. And I'm not going to give up until I do. What's the worst that can happen—I don't sleep? That was the problem to begin with.

When it comes to effective principles, you have to work them until they work in you. Period.

The habits I am going to share with you are time-tested. They are known as Sleep Hygiene. I practice them every night and this is why I get excellent sleep every time. Don't take these sleep practices lightly, overlooking them for a pill for tonight. If you do, you'll always be looking for a pill for tonight.

Sleep Hygiene Habit #1: Go to bed at the same time each night, or go to bed when tired.

Try to go to bed at roughly the same time each night. I say "roughly" because being 100 percent exact each night can be tough with fluctuating schedules. So as not to get hung up on time to the exact second, you want to try your best in general to get used to a routine. Your body likes that sort of thing—routines. I didn't say it in my heading, but ideally you want to try to wake up at the same time each morning as well. Again, you are creating a routine and you'll find that your body will start getting up whether or not you set your alarm clock, as it gets in the habit of sleeping the same amount each night.

An alternative solution to going to bed at the same time each night is going to bed when tired. If you can afford to, going to bed when your body tells you it is tired and subsequently waking up when your body tells you it's time to get up is an option too. Even here, you'll find that the summation of hours will end up being uniform each night. This type of option works best if your life affords you the luxury of not having to routinely report somewhere each morning at an exact time. This works well for those who set their own schedule.

This option eliminates the concern with not meeting a particular time for sleep onset, which I think causes a lot of people anxiety when they don't fall asleep by a certain time. When you're not tired, do something else fun and productive instead of worrying about why you haven't fallen asleep yet. Likewise, for those who wake up in the middle of the night, this alternative, again, takes the pressure off an individual because now, one can wake up at 3 a.m. and go and do something, going back to bed when their body again says they are tired. However, with people whose schedules are preset, waking up at 3 a.m. can be very anxiety-provoking, knowing you have to be somewhere at 7 a.m. and yet, you still need complete sleep restoration before you start the day. This alternative can be a nice comfort for those whose schedule can allow it.

Sleep Hygiene Habit #2: Before you go to bed ... relax!

I tell my patients all the time that your mind is like a pond that needs to be stilled. Like a pond—even in the most serene pond—there are always ripples going on in the water. Likewise, your brain is always undergoing activity. However when we sleep, the activity slows as compared to full wakefulness. In deep sleep, Delta wave activity are the predominant waveforms recorded by an electroencephalogram (EEG). These waves are high-amplitude, very low-frequency waves that are registered on EEG recordings mostly in stage 4 sleep (the deepest phase). When we are wide awake, Beta waves predominate, which are waves that are high frequency. As we relax and eventually fall to sleep, our brain waveforms go from Beta waves (15-30 hz), to Alpha waves (9-14 hz), to Theta waves (4-8 hz), and finally to Delta waves (1-3 hz). Concomitantly, the decrease in waveform frequency coincides with our increasing relaxed state as we eventually slip off to sleep.

It is my recommendation that as we prepare for bed, we must discover what causes each one of us to relax the best. For some, it is listening to quiet music; for others, drinking warm tea. But whatever it is, you must practice it. When you do this, the pond of your mind goes from choppy water to motionless, still water. If you are searching for a relaxation technique, here is one to try: sip some warm tea with honey and real lemongrass. Not only will this smell great, but before you know it, you will be dozing off to dream land.

Sleep Hygiene Habit #3: Think on something good.

One of the top three complaints I hear when it comes to insomnia is racing thoughts! Racing thoughts only seem to bother us when we are still. During the day, they shuffle around like sediment in a juice bottle virtually going unnoticed, however, it is when we get still (like when we are trying to go to bed) that these thoughts rise to the top of our minds, like sediment falling to the bottom of a bottle of juice previously shaken. Now, we have to deal with Aunt Sue's issue, the broken washing machine and the worry about that health concern … etc. These racing thoughts can and will prevent you from getting into Delta sleep. So what do you do? Deal with them.

My suggestion is to keep a journal and make two columns. On the left, write down the concern. On the right, put down a possible solution. Then close the book and start to relax, eventually going to sleep, knowing when you wake up you are going to act on the possible solution you wrote down in the right column. And when you relax, think on something good! When you do this, it fills the void of worry with the something good that you are thinking about. Failure to think on something good is like saying, "Racing thoughts … where are you? Come on back! I'm over here!" When I think on something good just before I go to bed, it leaves my last wakeful moment spent on something pleasant and I find it easier to relax and slip into sleep. Consider this!

Sleep Hygiene Habit #4: Kick out the TV.

Kick that TV out! (Of the bedroom. Not the house.) Listen, you may think your bedroom TV has nothing to do with your sleep because you swear you turn it off when you go to sleep. But let me tell you … so much of your sleep is habit and subconscious, it's not funny! Even though you turn off the TV, just the mere thought that it's there and the option that you can turn it on if you just want to *quickly* check the weather, is the same as just *quickly* throwing a small little pebble into the water and starting a ripple effect. Once water ripples, everything is affected. And even if you don't turn back on the TV, just the thought that you can, even subconsciously, is a pebble in the pond all in itself.

Just don't do it. If you're having trouble with sleep, just kick out the TV and watch it another time in another room. This is exactly what I do.

Sleep Hygiene Habit #5: Stop reading in bed.

Yeah, I know, reading in bed is the national favorite pastime. But if you want to get sleep, you cannot afford to make it *your* pastime. Read somewhere else, like your home library or office. Don't let the reading activity keep you from going from Beta wave to Delta wave. Stop the high-frequency brain activity!

Sleep Hygiene Habit #6: Eliminate caffeine.

"But the caffeine was during the earlier part of the day!" Yeah, but you can't sleep. Listen, if you have a sleep problem, why not do anything and everything to get some Zs? Drink decaffeinated whatever. You have nothing to lose. Again, caffeine is associated with insomnia, headaches and even high blood pressure. Why not just make this a non-factor— drink some decaf tea (with lemongrass and honey) and go to town— Dreamtown, that is!

Stop the high-frequency brain activity!

Sleep Hygiene Habit #7: Go to a massage room.

Literally, go to a spa. Not for a massage (though you might as well since you are there). But go to a massage room and look. What do you see? Usually what you'll find is a relaxing environment with dim lights and gentle music, the perfect relaxation environment. Question: Why isn't your bedroom a carbon copy? Get my point? You have to make your bedroom a sort of refuge for you and your spouse. I always tell husbands and wives that the bedroom should only be for two things: sleep and intimacy. Anything else defeats the purpose and your sleep. Kick out all the bills, newspapers, telephone and anything anxiety-provoking. You won't see these things in the massage parlor, so don't find them in your bedroom.

Practice

Practice these habits even on sleep medication until you no longer need the sleep medication. You have nothing to lose. You can't lose sleep because, again, that was the problem in the first place. But what you can gain is empowerment and control of when and how well you sleep and that, my friend, is everything! I practice these habits and that is why I have control of my sleep, like flipping off and on a light switch. Don't say, "I've tried it and it doesn't work." Work it again! Work it until it works, even if it takes 100 years. That's the attitude you must have when you apply principles that are proven. You cannot afford to get rid of principles that make good, common sense even if things don't seem to be working in the immediate. You have to keep going!

Practicing the Laws of Elite Health

Move. **E**at. **D**rink. **S**leep. Or … MEDS. These four laws are your MEDS. These are the laws you must take every day. They are the foundation to Elite Health. These four laws, when practiced, activate the benefit of elite wellness in your life. They are so basic and rudimentary that they are often underestimated. Like I said before, they are so common that their benefits are so uncommon! This is why I almost have to keep my patients from rolling their eyes when they come in with a cold and I tell them, "Make sure you Move, Eat, Drink, and Sleep!" Usually, my patients are like, "I'm doing this already." Uh ah …, you're not. That's why 75 percent of you are dehydrated all the time. You think you are practicing the laws, but you're not. So I tell my patients when they are under the weather to go overboard on their MEDS—the laws, not the pills—so that they ensure they are really and truly practicing the principles of elite health.

But don't just take MEDS when you are under the weather, take them when you are over the weather! This is really how you put a power stroke in your daily life, by practicing health-empowering principles that excel your life!

Listen, I can tell you that at least 75 percent of people are not doing them. I'll go higher than that: I find that only the top two to three percent of my patients routinely take their MEDS! When you take your MEDS, this is how you don't have to take *your meds*. That's what most of you want anyway. I hear it all the time, "Doc, you know … uh, um … I really don't like taking a lot of medication." Well, guess what? I'm going to put you on a lot of medication if you don't start getting a grip on your cholesterol, your high blood pressure and your weight, because I don't want you to be sick and in the hospital!

This is really how you put a power stroke in your daily life, by practicing health-empowering principles that excel your life!

Your perspective must be that *I am going to take my MEDS because I want to be better each day in my life than the day before—health-wise and overall.* Listen, today I woke up and said my daily affirmation that "Today is going to be the best day of my life!" About 30 minutes later when I was driving to work, I thought to myself, *Why do I really want to make today better? Why do I want to push? Why am I staying driven? Why do I keep going?* Before I got to the clinic, I answered this question in my head. The answer was simply this: The attainment of *better* was a reward I could not bear to miss. Meaning, knowing and experiencing myself being better (for me and others) was so great a reward (to be experienced) that failure to push to get there (or failure to get there) was an outcome unacceptable for me to imagine.

Bottom line, friend: You have to be better for you and for me. You have to have things in front of you *to do* so worthwhile that not being better today as compared to yesterday is unacceptable. Your health has to be elite for you. Your elite health may not be the same as mine—and that's OK—but it has to be your best health so that you do your life. You have to see your life as something so precious to live out that you'll do whatever it takes to buy more time on this earth through healthy living, so that you can finish your goal. And finishing is everything.

You have to see your life as something so precious to live out that you'll do whatever it takes to buy more time on this earth through healthy

living, so that you can finish your goal.

I want you to finish to be satisfied. Failure to finish, and to finish on time, is like that plane leaving Orlando and landing in Vegas, though it was supposed to land in L.A. (or like landing in L.A. two hours late!). If you'll strive to be better, you'll start completing more of your goals, helping more people and allowing a whole new level of energy to usher in to your life, all the while feeling healthier, more dynamic and simply better in every way. Friend, strive to be better, on the platform of your elite health!

Chapter Twelve

I think that what it all comes down to is understanding that you have something to offer—something to give. And this service that only you can provide in such a unique way has your own imprint on it. Your mark. And this is what you must leave on this world. No one can replace you, but you can be replaced. However, if you'll see your life as an offer—your entire life—you'll choose to stand up and unleash all the talents, all the abilities and all the things that you have to express to those around you.

This is why we cannot afford to waste any more time with our life. And this is exactly why you need energy. Energy *to do*. Failure to see your life as a blessing to others rips out the guts to the global view of your life.

I see people all the time who get so distracted by things that don't matter. Concerns, issues, fears—excuses. They take the attitude that, "I should be doing this, I should be doing that," but they never do. I learned that it is a waste of time to motivate someone like this. If this is you, it's simply time to decide to go one way or another—to stay where you are or to board the plane to your next level. It's up to you. No cheerleading. No rah rah. Board or stay. And I understand that there will be people who stay where they are. People who stay in the land of tiredness, the land of obesity, the land of low energy. I don't feel for these people, for like me, they have the opportunity to choose to take that one-way ticket out of there. They just don't.

Having Energy To Give

I want you to have energy. My message is that if you'll see your life as one to be lived to accomplish a certain task, to travel a certain journey, to accomplish certain things, then—and only then—will you see the need to live your life in such a healthy way as to provide you more time on this earth to finish your task. When you do this, you'll no longer side-step healthy living for short-term gratification. You'll no longer try to get through the day or just live to satisfy your feelings; but instead, your life— so that you'll have health for tomorrow, the next decade and beyond. You'll plan strategically, you'll eat with purpose, you'll stay fit for the long haul when you see your life as something to accomplish. This is what I meant when I said in *Boarding* that you do not just want more energy or the latest and greatest energy drink. You want passion, more awareness and focus, and plain ol' get-up-and-go (Inspiration, Concentration, Execution). And to have this, you have to think globally about your life.

That's why I tell my smokers that you do not want to smoke. Yes, it makes you feel good. Yes, you are addicted, only not like you think. You are addicted because you have allowed your mind, will, emotions, intellect and imagination (your soul), your body and yourself to wrap itself around something you plain ol' enjoy. That's it in a nutshell. The key word in that last statement is "you have allowed," and do not let any other high-minded individual tell you differently—that it's not your fault, that you couldn't help it, that it's an addiction, and any other type of mess that simply undermines your power as a person to make a choice, board the plane and fly off to your new life.

Don't get me wrong, I'm not saying you don't need help. You do. But the bottom line is that no one can make the decision for you. In order to smoke a cigarette, you have to walk over to the package of cigarettes, open the package, take out a lighter, put the cigarette in your mouth, light the cigarette and smoke. All of those steps involve *you doing something*, and nothing *doing something to you* to make you do what you do—smoke. Whose fault is that? Only yours. But the way our world is, you are blamed when you are telling someone that it's your fault. Sometimes in life things happen that are not your fault; then again, there are decisions we make that are our fault. And we have to answer to it when it is. Why are you overweight, why are you not reaching for your goals, why do you not have goals, why are you tired, why are you not focused? Why, why, why? You've got the answer.

I know I am coming off direct. I'm trying to leave an impression. I'm trying to make you think—deeper. I'm trying to cause you to have answers—for yourself.

Takeoff and Landing: The Two Most Important Parts of Your Day

I ask people all the time: What are the two most important times during air travel on a plane? Everyone always answers this question on first attempt—takeoff and landing. The flying in between matters; it's just not as important as how a plane starts and finishes. Interesting enough, most of the time in mid-flight, the plane is usually on automatic pilot and not manual control. The point I am trying to make about this is that when it comes to making changes in your life and going to new levels, it's all about how you wake up in the morning and go to bed at night. Your routines matter—this is one of the main themes of this book. In Section Two I talked about concentration; that making a schedule and honing the routine is essential to accomplishing goals in life. But just having a schedule is not enough because in order to go higher in life by making better decisions and incorporating change, you have to think it through.

Thinking through time is at night; I call this fix time, where you are fixing your thinking for tomorrow to take off and go somewhere new. And in the morning, a part of your routine should be to review what you thought through—that's taking off right. These two times of your day are the most important because it sets the tone for your day—and summing it up, it eventually sets the tone for your life. Your daily routines are the footprints to where your life is eventually going. So, if you want to work on quitting smoking, eating better or losing weight, think at night how you are going to make more improved decisions tomorrow. And then tomorrow, review and finally execute the change.

Your daily routines are the footprints to where your life is eventually going.

If you do not do this, you'll only do what you have done and you won't take off to somewhere new. It's a guarantee. If you do not take off and land properly daily in your life, you will not go somewhere new. There is no hope of rising higher if you fail to think things through; you cannot execute something new.

Want More Energy? Take a Vacation

I want to leave you with something else, my friend; something I think is very important. Something I think is often done without purpose. Take a vacation. You have to get away to have more energy. On this journey of accomplishment in your life, you have to know when to rest. You're not resting to go somewhere tropical and get drunk, for this would be vacation without purpose. You are resting to experience something new, to recharge, refresh—giving rest to your soul, body and self so that you can return to your business of doing your life. When you vacation, you are doing so with purpose while you are having fun. The problem with many is that whenever I say you are doing something "with purpose"—eating with purpose, exercising with purpose, vacationing with purpose—the problem is that the "purpose" part of the phrase to some means doing something without the fun. Think higher! The fun part of it is the experience in itself and that it is also leading you one step closer to the accomplishment of the goals in your life. This is really what connecting the dots is all about.

The WellSpring

This chapter is a little different than the three prior in this section (Execution). I know. It's the last chapter. This chapter really is not about calories, nutrition or health stuff. As you can see, it's not about heart rate, medications or disease. I know people can be tired and have low energy because of anemia, sleep apnea and other metabolic disorders and issues. I am well aware of it. I see it all the time as a doctor. And I want to say that is why having a physical and lab work every year are so vitally important because there truly are other factors involved in total health. Taking this into account, you must decide to take action for yourself. You must decide to execute your life. You must decide to do your *to dos*.

The title of this book, "WellSpring," literally means "a source or supply of anything, especially when considered inexhaustible." Through this book, I have taken you on a journey to set up your life to be a source or supply of energy considered inexhaustible. I have stressed the importance of developing a systematic way of living designed to provide you with perpetual energy *to do* your life. If you find your inspiration, take time to concentrate, and also choose to execute, you can live a life that continually gives back more drive and energy to you in order *to do* your life. That's why the energy you want is more than the instant energy you think you need. You won't find this type of energy in a beverage. You won't find this type of energy in a pill. You'll only find this energy in you according to the type of healthy choices you make.

You're here now … in the WellSpring. We've landed. You may not have realized our gradual descent. But here we are—our new place. Conceptually, we've left the land of tiredness and we've come into the WellSpring. We've arrived. We've finished. You know what to do. You know how to do. The only question is: Will you do?

Afterword

More

This is how you must think: More. What's next? Where are we going now? Friend, it's time to take off again. Living in the WellSpring is always about taking off and landing and going somewhere new. Ceasing to go higher and to experience new places short-circuits the energy necessary to flow through you. It stops the currency of energy, so to speak. I want to push you to go higher. Your attitude should be, *Look what we've accomplished! Great! But now I need to accomplish more in this area or that area. Or, I want to see what's over the next horizon.* There's always something More.

I've enjoyed traveling with you, my friend. This has been a wonderful experience. Writing this book has meant that I have now accomplished one of the *to dos* in my life. I've crossed another thing off my list. This has been literally a nine-month project, but it started many years before. I have enjoyed being your pilot on this flight; a pilot and coach to you, so to speak. But like I have been this to you, I too, have had a pilot and coach.

Dr. Stacia Pierce, whom I have introduced to you throughout this book, has been my pilot and my coach. She has pushed me to unleash this literary work to you. She is a phenomenal success coach and inspiration to millions nationwide. But most importantly to me, she is the person who saw More in me than I could see. And she required More than I thought I could give. Coach, to you I say, thank you. For if it had not been for you, this book would still be on the shelf of my heart and not on the shelf in the homes of my readers (or better yet, in their hands with them reading it). Coach Stacia, I say, thank you.

I am very proud of myself for finishing this work. Again, it was an item on my life's list of *to dos* that I'll be able to say I completed before departing. During this project there were many days where I had no physical energy. In fact, this book in a way was draining because I poured myself into it and onto each page. The difference was, this type of drain was not the type of drain without inspiration, because the goal of writing this book caused me to be driven and to look at each day with the eye of something to accomplish, day in and day out. I had WellSpring energy, literally. And to harness this energy—to cultivate it—I had to shape my days in a way so as to direct my strength toward accomplishing this task—finishing the book.

I literally had to block out time devoted to writing so that I could accomplish my goal. This not only took inspiration but also concentration. The execution part of it is that I had to do it to get it done. In other words, I had to release or let go of my energy (a.k.a burn it up) in order to make progress. Instead of keeping all this energy to myself and doing nothing, I had to put this energy to work and write. So I did. And the end result is that I finished WellSpring: The Energy Secrets To Do the Good Life. And guess what? Now I'm driven to do more! I'm not energy depleted. I am energy repleted. And this is because I am living in the WellSpring.

So, what will you do? Will you choose to do what's on your *to dos* and do More? Or will you stay where you are and allow your circumstances, your disabilities or your excuses to drain the energy you have left? Friend, you have a choice. You can stay there or take the ticket and board the plane and leave. I want you to board the plane and be off to More. You can fly over tiredness and have more energy. You can accomplish your dreams. You can be driven *to do* though physically tired. You can do more if you're willing. Like I left you pondering in my last chapter … what will you do? Now Boarding.

Bibliography

Colbert, Don, M.D., *What You Don't Know May Be Killing You!* Siloam Press, 2000.

Colbert, Don, M.D., *Toxic Relief.* Siloam, 2003.

Johnson, Chris. *Meal Patterning.* First Printing, 2003.

Johnson, Chris. *On Target Living Nutrition: The Power of Feeling Your Best.* On Target Living, 2007.

Kiyosaki, Robert. *Unfair Advantage.* Plata Publishing, 2011.

Lawrence, Peter F, Senior Editor. *Essentials of General Surgery.* Lippincott Williams & Wilkins, 2000.

Livestrong.com a proud partner of the Lance Armstrong Foundation. *Target Heart Rate.* Demand Media, 2012.

Movies References: *Runaway Bride; Rocky IV; Good Will Hunting*

Pierce, Stacia, Ph.D., *The Power of Vision: Frame Your Future with Your Imagination.* Life House Press, 2004.

Pierce, Stacia, Ph.D., *The Millionaire's Dream Book Success Attraction System.* Ultimate Lifestyle Enterprises, LLC, 2011.

Pierce, James, Ph.D., Related speaking topics including: *Meditation: Visualizing, Verbalizing, Memorizing.*

Wikipedia: The Free Encyclopedia. Related articles searches include: *Calorie; Fats; Proteins; Biochemistry; Food Energy; Carbohydrates; Lipolysis; Capacitance.*